# Merlin Book of Logic Puzzles

# Merlin Book of Logic Puzzles

Margaret C. Edmiston

Sterling Publishing Co., Inc. New York

**Library of Congress Cataloging-in-Publication Data**

Edmiston, Margaret C.
Merlin book of logic puzzles / by Margaret C. Edmiston.
p. cm.
Includes index.
ISBN 0-8069-8220-9
1. Mathematical recreations. I. Title.
QA95.E36 1991
793.7'4—dc20 91-24019
CIP

10 9 8 7 6 5 4 3 2 1

Published in 1991 by Sterling Publishing Company, Inc.
387 Park Avenue South, New York, N.Y. 10016

Distributed in Canada by Sterling Publishing
% Canadian Manda Group, P.O. Box 920, Station U
Toronto, Ontario, Canada M8Z 5P9
Distributed in Great Britain and Europe by Cassell PLC
Villiers House, 41/47 Strand, London WC2N 5JE, England
Distributed in Australia by Capricorn Link Ltd.
P.O. Box 665, Lane Cove, NSW 2066
*Manufactured in the United States of America*


Sterling ISBN 0-8069-8220-9

# CONTENTS

# A FEW WORDS FROM THE AUTHOR

The suggestion to use the Merlin legend as a backdrop for this logic puzzle book was made to me by Sterling Publishing Company editor Sheila Anne Barry. I accepted her idea at once, recognizing the rich variety of puzzles that could be set within the context of the Merlin legend and the associated Arthurian romance.

One part of the Merlin legend has Merlin serving as the wise mentor and magical helper of the young king Arthur. It was this aspect of the legend, together with the familiar stories of the doings of King Arthur's knights, that prompted the traditional logic puzzles of Chapter II, wherein the young king must solve puzzles in which his own knights, or the squires of some of those knights, appear as characters.

A rather different aspect of the Merlin legend places Merlin in the pre-Christian folklore of the Celts as a culture hero and Druid. It seemed only natural to associate with this Merlin such supernatural beings as fairies and elves—and, yes, even imprisoned princesses and monstrous dragons. From this aspect of the legend come many of the puzzles of Chapters III and IV.

Other characters associated directly with aspects of the Merlin legend, or indirectly with the times in which Merlin lived, also appear here and there in this book: sorcerer's apprentices, Saxon spies, kings, and ogres among them.

All that is required to solve most of the puzzles within these pages are paper and pencil or pen, a fresh mind, and a keen enjoyment of the challenge of a good puzzle. No special training is required, although in a very few cases the solver who knows simple algebra will have an advantage.

Happy solving.

Margaret C. Edmiston

# CHAPTER I
# COIN OF THE REALM

*Merlin Challenges a Prospective Apprentice*

One day Merlin was approached by a young man who said, "Great Merlin, I fain would become a sorcerer. Will you take me as your pupil?"

Merlin was accustomed to such inquiries. Many in the kingdom had made similar requests, but few had their requests granted. However, Merlin was in good spirits on this particular day, and the eager supplicant was noble of brow, so Merlin replied, "I am always seeking virtuous and bright young men as students. Your virtue cannot be known to me at once, but your intelligence can be easily tested. If your wit be strong enough to solve the ten puzzles that I will now present to you, I will take you on as an trial apprentice, whereupon you must begin to prove your virtue."

The puzzles given to the prospective apprentice to solve are presented in this chapter. The young man in question found some to be amazingly simple and others more difficult, but he was able to solve them all. Now you can test your wits on the same puzzles. (If you find that a puzzle seems familiar, it may be because it is a new version of a classic puzzle or an old puzzle presented in a new way.)

## 1. MISLEADING LABELS

Three chests contain coins. One is labelled "gold," a second "bronze," a third "gold or silver." One chest contains gold coins only, another silver coins only, and the third bronze coins only, but all the chests are incorrectly labelled. How many chests must be opened to determine the contents of each chest?

*Solving suggestions on pages 17–20*
*Answers on pages 21–25*

## 2. COLORFUL COINS

Coins painted blue, green, red, or yellow have the following characteristics: on a balance scale, one blue coin balances three green coins; one green coin balances four yellow ones plus one red one; and one red one balances two yellow ones. How many yellow coins will it take to balance one blue one?

## 3. COINS FOR HIS DAUGHTERS

A king distributed some gold coins among his three daughters in the following manner. To his eldest daughter he gave one half of the coins plus one coin. To his middle daughter he gave one half the remaining coins plus one coin. Finally, to his youngest daughter he gave one half the coins remaining plus one coin, after which the king had no coins left. How many gold coins did he have to start with?

## 4. HOW MANY COINS?

Aken, Bal, and Col had 21 coins among them. First, Col gave Aken two of his coins. Then Aken gave Bal one of his coins. Finally, Bal gave Col one of his coins. The result was that all three ended up with the same number of coins. How many coins did each of the three begin with?

## 5. WHICH IS THE HEAVIER COIN?

One day one of Merlin's apprentices was polishing a collection of 14 gold coins, all of which seemed to be identical in every way. However, one of the 14 weighed a fraction more than the others. While polishing the heavier coin, the new apprentice accidentally dropped it. With a clunk, it fell into the pile of the other coins. Unable to identify it, the unfortunate apprentice went in tears to confess to Merlin what he had done. "Tears will not solve the problem," said Merlin. "Here is a balance scale. In three weighings, you should be able to identify the heavier coin. Take note that the scale is not sturdy enough to weigh more than four coins to a side."

How can the heavier coin be identified in three weighings?

*Solving suggestions on pages 17–20*
*Answers on pages 1–25*

## 6. A MORE DIFFICULT BALANCING PROBLEM

Suppose there are nine coins, one of which weighs *either* just a bit more *or* just a bit less than the other eight, which all weigh the same. The odd coin is somehow confused with the others. Identify this coin in three weighings and, at the same time, determine whether it is heavier or lighter than the others.

## 7. GOLD COINS IN THE CHEST

Merlin explained this puzzle as follows: "Here is a chest. It might contain some gold coins or it might not. I am told that if it contains gold coins it is labelled with a true statement, but that if it does not contain gold coins it is labelled with a false statement."

The statement reads:

THIS CHEST DOES NOT CONTAIN GOLD COINS

What can be deduced from the statement and the given facts?

# 8. MORE GOLD COINS IN THE CHEST

Each of three chests is labelled with a statement. One of the chests contains gold coins, one contains silver coins, and one contains bronze coins. The statement on the chest containing the gold coins is a true statement, but the statements on the other two chests are both false. The chests are labelled as follows.

| A | B | C |
|---|---|---|
| This chest does not contain the silver coins | The gold coins are in chest C | This chest contains the bronze coins |

Which one contains the gold coins? What kind of coins are in each of the other chests?

*Solving suggestions on pages 17–20*
*Answers on pages 21–25*

## 9. GOLD OR CLAY?

Three chests contain either coins of gold or worthless lumps of clay. The following is known:

1. If chest C contains clay, then chest B contains gold.
2. If chest A contains gold, then chest C contains clay.
3. If chest B contains clay, then chest A contains gold.

Which chest, if any, can be labelled as to its contents?

## 10. A LITTLE PROBABILITY

A pot contains one gold coin and one silver coin. A second pot contains two gold coins and one silver one. A coin is drawn from the first pot (without any deliberate selection; the probability of drawing one of the coins is the same as that of drawing the other) and dropped into the second. Then a coin is drawn from the second pot (without any deliberate selection). What is the probability that the coin drawn from the second pot will be a gold coin?

*Answers on pages 21–25*

# SOLVING SUGGESTIONS

**1. Misleading Labels.** Any information would give away the answer.

**2. Colorful Coins.** Let **b** stand for one blue coin, **g** for one green coin, and so forth. Write equations (equality statements) using the information given. For example: **b = 3g** (meaning **b** equals 3 times **g**). Then use substitution to arrive at the answer.

**3. Coins for His Daughters.** Begin at the end—the king gave his youngest daughter half the coins plus one coin, and then had no coins left. Can you see that the king must have had two coins? Once you verify this, figure out how many coins he had when he gave some to his middle daughter. If you can't apply algebra, try trial and error.

**4. How Many Coins?** Use the fact that each had the same number of coins in the end.

**5. Which Is the Heavier Coin?** As a first step, weigh four coins against four coins. The two sides will balance or they will not balance. Figure out what you would do if a balance results from this weighing and what you would do if one side is heavier than the other.

**6. A More Difficult Balancing Problem.** No hints here. It's quite possible that your first attempt to solve this puzzle won't be successful, but don't let that deter you. Let your imagination lead you.

**7. and 8. Gold Coins in the Chest.** Just look for contradictions. Any other hints at solving would give away the answers.

**9. Gold or Clay?** With three chests, each of which might contain either gold or clay, there are eight possible combinations. Make a chart showing these, as follows, where "g" stands for gold and "c" for clay. Then eliminate all combinations which contradict the given facts.

POSSIBLE COMBINATIONS

| | 1 | 2 | 3 | 4 | 5 | 6 | 7 | 8 |
|---|---|---|---|---|---|---|---|---|
| A | g | g | g | c | g | c | c | c |
| B | g | g | c | g | c | g | c | c |
| C | g | c | g | g | c | c | g | c |

**10. A Little Probability.** Enumerate all the possibilities, using G 1 and S 1 for the two coins in pot #1, and G 2a, G 2b, and S 2 for the three coins in pot #2. One such possibility, for example, would be to draw the gold coin from pot #1 (so that pot #2 would then contain G 1, G 2a, G 2b, and S 2), then draw the silver coin (S 2) from pot #2.

# ANSWERS

**1. Misleading Labels.** It is not necessary to open any of the chests. The chest labelled "gold or silver" is mislabelled, so it contains neither gold nor silver; it contains bronze coins. The one labelled "gold" is mislabelled and doesn't contain bronze, so must contain silver. Thus, the one labelled bronze contains gold.

**2. Colorful Coins.** 18 yellow coins balance one blue one. Let **b** stand for one blue coin; **g** stand for one green coin; **y** stand for one yellow coin; and **r** stand for one red coin. Then, we have:

| | |
|---|---|
| $\mathbf{b = 3g}$ | (note: this means **b** equals 3 times **g**) |
| $\mathbf{b = 3\ (4y + r)}$ | (substituting **4y + r** for **g**) |
| $\mathbf{b = 12y + 3r}$ | (by multiplication) |
| $\mathbf{b = 12y + 3\ (2y)}$ | (substituting **2y** for **r**) |
| $\mathbf{b = 12y + 6y}$ | (multiplication) |
| $\mathbf{b = 18y}$ | (addition) |

**3. Coins for His Daughters.** The king had 14 coins to begin with. Start with the fact that the king gave his youngest daughter half of the coins remaining (after he had given some to his middle daughter), plus one coin, and then had no coins left. From this fact, we know that if the king had given his youngest daughter exactly half of the coins remaining, he would have had *one* coin left. Thus half the coins remaining just before he gave away the last of them has to be one coin. So the number of coins the king had left after giving coins to his middle daughter must have been two.

Now let x = the number of coins remaining after he had given coins to his eldest daughter. We have $\mathbf{x - (x/2 + 1) = 2; x/2 - 1 = 2; x/2 = 3; x = 6}$. So the number of coins the king had left after giving coins to his eldest daughter was six. Now let y = the number of coins the king had to start with and we have $\mathbf{y - (y/2 + 1) = 6; y/2 - 1 = 6; y/2 = 7; y = 14}$. So the king started with 14 coins. First he gave eight to his eldest daughter ($\mathbf{(\frac{1}{2} \times 14) + 1 = 8}$), leaving six. Then, of the six remaining he gave four to his middle daughter ($\mathbf{(\frac{1}{2} \times 6) + 1 = 4}$), leaving two; finally he gave both of the two remaining coins to his youngest daughter ($\mathbf{(\frac{1}{2} \times 2) + 1 = 2}$).

**4. How Many Coins?** Aken had six, Bal had seven, Col had eight. Each ended up with the same number of coins. Since there were 21 coins in total, each ended up with seven. After Aken gave Bal one of his coins, he had seven left. So just before he gave a coin to Bal, Aken had eight. Before that he had been given two coins by Col. So Aken had six coins to start with. When Col was given one coin by Bal, that brought him up to seven coins. So Col had six coins before that. But he had previously given two coins to Aken. So he must have had eight to begin with. Since Col started out with eight coins and Aken with six, for a total of 14 coins, it follows that Bal began with 21 minus 14, or 7, coins.

**5. Which Is the Heavier Coin?** Number the 14 coins "1," "2," "3," etc. Weigh coins 1, 2, 3, and 4 against coins 5, 6, 7, and 8. If they don't balance, the side containing the heavier coin is apparent. Without loss of generality assume it is the side containing coins 1, 2, 3, and 4. Weigh coins 1 and 2 against coins 3 and 4. This second weighing will identify the heavier side; without loss of generality, assume the side containing coins 1 and 2 is heavier. For the third weighing put coin 1 on one side of the balance and coin 2 on the other; the heavier coin is then identified. Now suppose that on the first weighing (coins 1, 2, 3, and 4 vs. coins 5, 6, 7, and 8) the two sides balance, so we know that the heavier coin is one of the unweighed coins: 9, 10, 11, 12, 13, or 14. Weigh coins 9, 10, and 11 against coins 12, 13, and 14. This second weighing identifies the heavier side; without loss of generality, assume it is the side containing coins 9, 10, and 11. For the third weighing compare coins 9 and 10. If they don't balance, the heavier coin is apparent; if they do balance, the heavier coin is the one marked with the numeral 11.

**6. A More Difficult Balancing Problem.** Number the nine coins with the numerals 1 through 9. Weigh coins 1, 2, and 3 against coins 4, 5, and 6. If they balance, the odd coin is 7 or 8 or 9. Now weigh coins 1, 2 and 7 against coins 3, 8, and 9 (we know from the first weighing that coins 1, 2, and 3 all weigh the same). If the side containing 1, 2, and 7 is lighter, we know that either 7 is light, or 8 or 9 is heavy. For the third weighing, compare coins 8 and 9. If they balance, 7 is the odd coin and it is light. If they don't balance, the odd coin is the one on the heavier side. Now suppose that in weighing 1, 2, and 7 against 3, 8, and 9 that the side containing 1, 2, and 7 is heavier. This means that 7 is heavy, or 8 or 9 is light. Weigh 8 against 9. If they balance, the odd coin is 7, and it is heavy. If they don't balance, the odd coin is the one on the lighter side.

Now go back to the first weighing and suppose that in weighing 1, 2, and 3 against 4, 5, and 6, a balance was not obtained. Assume without loss of generality that the side containing coins 1, 2, and 3 is light. Then we would know that the odd coin is either 1 or 2 or 3 and is light or is 4, or 5, or 6, and is heavy, while coins 7, 8, and 9 all weigh the same. Weigh 1, 2, 4, and 7 against 3, 5, 8, and 9. If the side containing 1, 2, 4, and 7 is light it means that either 1 or 2 is light or 5 is heavy. If the side containing 1, 2, 4, and 7 is heavy, it means that either 4 is heavy or 3 is light. In the first case, weigh 1 against 2; if they balance, 5 is the odd coin and it is heavy; if they don't balance, the lighter coin is the odd coin. In the second case, weigh 4 against 7; if they balance, 3 is the odd coin and it is light; if they don't balance, 4 is the odd coin and it is heavy.

**7. Gold Coins in the Chest.** We would conclude that the premises given were incorrect. The statement on the chest presents us with a paradox. If the chest contains gold coins it is supposed to be labelled with a true statement, yet, in this case, the statement would be false. If the chest does not contain gold coins, it is supposed to be labelled with a false statement, yet, in this case, the statement would be true.

**8. More Gold Coins in the Chest. A** contains the gold coins; **B** contains the bronze coins; **C** contains the silver coins. The statement on chest **B** must be false, for if it were true we are presented with a contradiction. The gold coins would be in chest **C** because the statement on **B** is true, but would have to be in chest **B** because the true statement is on the chest containing the gold coins. The statement on chest **C** must also be untrue, for if it were true, it would contain bronze coins, whereas we are told that the one chest with a true statement contains the gold coins. Therefore, by elimination, the chest with the true statement is **A**; hence, **A** contains the gold coins. Then, since the statement on **C** is false, the bronze coins are in chest **B**; by elimination, chest **C** contains the silver coins.

**9. Gold or Clay?** Chest B contains gold.

POSSIBLE COMBINATIONS

| | 1 | 2 | 3 | 4 | 5 | 6 | 7 | 8 |
|---|---|---|---|---|---|---|---|---|
| A: | G | G | G | C | G | C | C | C |
| B: | G | G | C | G | C | G | C | C |
| C: | G | C | G | G | C | C | G | C |

Statement 1 eliminates 5 and 8. Statement 2 eliminates 1 and 3. Statement 3 eliminates 7. The remaining possibilities are 2, 4, and 6. In all three cases B contains gold, but we see that both A and C could contain either gold or clay; so all we can conclude is that B contains gold.

**10. A Little Probability.** 5 in 8, or 5/8. The eight equally likely possibilities can be enumerated as follows, letting **G 1** represent the gold coin in pot #1, **S 1** the silver coin in pot #1, **G 2a** and **G 2b** the two gold coins in pot #2, and **S 2** the silver coin in pot #2.

DRAWN FROM

| Pot #1 | Pot #2 |
|---|---|
| G 1 | G 1 |
| G 1 | G 2a |
| G 1 | G 2b |
| G 1 | S 2 |
| S 1 | S 1 |
| S 1 | G 2a |
| S 1 | G 2b |
| S 1 | S 2 |

We see that in five cases the coin drawn from pot #2 is gold and in three cases it is silver; since each happening is equally likely, the probability of drawing a gold coin is 5/8.

# CHAPTER II
# MERLIN CHALLENGES ARTHUR

***With Traditional Logic Problems Involving Knights, Squires, and Other Characters***

One can easily believe that Merlin wanted Arthur to bc a wise king as well as a brave and noble one. To improve the young king's reasoning powers he might have challenged Arthur with the kinds of logic puzzles you will find in this chapter.

These logic puzzles are the kind that many people think of when they hear the term "logic problem," and, as such, they are the favorites of many.

## 1. THE NEW YEAR'S EVE BALL

On New Year's Eve each of the first four knights to arrive at the castle at Camelot for the final ball of the year was mounted on a magnificent charger adorned in trappings that were the principal color of each knight's banner. In no particular order, these knights were Sir Pure, Sir Good, Sir Pious, and Sir Venerable. From the clues that follow, Arthur was to deduce the order of arrival of the four knights and the major color of each knight's trappings: blue, gold, purple, or white.

1. The four knights were Sir Pious, the knight who arrived second, the knight whose horse wore white trappings, and Sir Pure.
2. Sir Pious did not arrive first, and Sir Venerable was not the knight who arrived just before him.
3. Sir Venerable's steed didn't wear white trappings.
4. Sir Good arrived just before the knight whose horse wore blue trappings, who wasn't Sir Pious.
5. Sir Pure's charger did not wear purple trappings.

*Solving suggestions on pages 43–49*
*Answers on pages 51–60*

# 2. WHO WON THE JOUSTING TOURNAMENT?

Merlin challenged the young king with this logic puzzle as the two of them were sitting in the stands at the jousting field. The problem was set forth as follows: at a recent jousting tournament in which a total of ten knights participated, the numbers 1 through 10 were assigned by lot to the knights. The tournament began with a contest between #1 and #2. The winner of that contest went on to

meet #3, and the winner of that second bout jousted against #4, and so forth. The last knight to remain unhorsed was the winner.

Arthur's task: to identify the participants in each of the nine matches, in order, and the winner of each, using the information given and the following additional clues.

1. Seven of the ten knights won no contests.
2. One contest was between #5 and #6.
3. One contest was between #7 and #9.
4. #2 did not joust against #4.

## 3. NAME THE KNIGHTS

Arthur may have been surprised when, just after he had solved the previous puzzle, Merlin asked him to deduce the names of the ten knights in the jousting contest. Merlin gave him the following clues, all of which pertain to the knights in puzzle #2. In alphabetical order, the knights were Sirs Bad, Black, Brave, Chaste, Glory, Good, Grand, Noble, Pure, and White.

1. Sir Pure's only contest was against Sir Black.
2. Sir Brave's only contest was against Sir Noble. Sir Brave wasn't #10.
3. Sir Good's single contest was four matches before that between Sir Noble and Sir Bad.
4. Sir Bad defeated Sir Grand.
5. Sir Chaste had the position number just before Sir White.
6. No two knights whose names begin with the letter B had consecutive position numbers.
7. Sir Glory and Sir Bad had consecutive numbers, in one order or the other.

*Solving suggestions on pages 43–49*
*Answers on pages 51–60*

# 4. THE RANKINGS OF THE SQUIRES

Arthur found this puzzle particularly fun to solve. His task: to determine how each of five judges, all knights, ranked each of five squires in terms of their overall promise as future knights.

The five judges were Sir Black, Sir Good, Sir Pure, Sir Noble, and Sir Wise. The five squires were Gort, Harl, Jol, Kal, and Lok. In determining their rankings, each knight gave a score of 5 to the squire he considered the most promising, a score of 4 to the squire he considered the next-most-promising, and so on, so that he gave a score of 1 to that squire he considered least promising. Thus, each squire received five scores. These were totaled to determine the "most promising squire of the year."

The following additional facts were made known to Arthur:

1. Sir Black gave a higher ranking to Harl than Sir Good did.
2. Sir Noble's score for Harl was higher than any other score Harl received.
3. Sir Black rated Kal as Sir Good rated Lok.
4. Sir Pure's score for Kal was half Sir Noble's score for Harl.
5. Three knights, Black, Good, and one other, assigned their highest rating of 5 to Jol.
6. Sir Wise's score of 2 went to Harl; Sir Noble's score of 2 went to Kal.
7. Sir Pure and Sir Noble gave their 5's to the same squire.
8. Lok's total score was 21 points; Lok received a lower score from Sir Black than from any other judge.
9. One squire received no score higher than 3; his one score of 3 was given by Sir Pure.

## 5. MIXED-UP MUGS

Each of five squires who share living quarters owns a distinctively-marked drinking mug. One morning the first of five to awaken was so groggy from a poor night of rest that he inadvertently used the wrong mug. The second squire to awaken found his mug gone, so he also used a mug that didn't belong to him. The final result was that every one of the five squires ended up using a mug that wasn't his own. The five squires were Arn, Gar, Hap, Pel, and Tul. The five mug designs were: a dragon, a horse, a shield, a sword, a mark of **X**. Arthur's task was to match each mug with the squire who owns it and the squire who used it on the day of the mix-up. The following facts were made known to Arthur:

1. The mug used by Pel belongs to the squire who drank from the mug with a horse painted on it.
2. The mug with the dragon picture was used by the squire who owns the mug with the sword design on it.
3. Tul either owns or used the mug with the picture of a shield on it.
4. Hap's mug was used by Arn.
5. Gar used the mug marked with an **X**, which doesn't belong to Arn.
6. The owner-user pair for any one mug was in no case the user-owner pair for another mug.
7. Either Tul borrowed Pel's mug, or Pel borrowed Tul's.

*Solving suggestions on pages 43–49*
*Answers on pages 51–60*

# 6. ROMANCE AMONG THE SQUIRES AND MAIDS

Let us envision Arthur and Merlin again sitting together in the stands of the jousting field enjoying a warm, sunny day, when suddenly two young lovers emerge from a path that feeds the woods beyond the field. The couple are walking cheek to cheek and holding hands. "Who are they?" asks Arthur.

Merlin replies: "One of the queen's maids and one of the knight's squires. They seem to be in love, don't they?" But the affairs of the heart were not always so agreeable for four of the maids and four of the squires. Not long ago, the situation was that although each loved some one person among the four of the opposite sex and was in turn loved by some one person among the four of the opposite sex, no maid loved the squire who loved her, and no squire loved the maid who loved him. The four maids were Elise, Fiona, Heloise, and Mary. The four squires were Balder, Court, Derwent, and Marc.

The task given to Arthur was to figure out the name of the maid each squire loved and the name of the squire each maid loved. Merlin gave Arthur the following clues:

1. Elise loved Balder.
2. The squire named Marc did not love the maid named Mary, nor did Mary love Marc.
3. Fiona was infatuated with the squire who loved Heloise.
4. Marc loved the maid who loved Court.
5. Derwent loved the maid who loved Marc.

# 7. MERLIN AND THE DISGUISES

One day Merlin, Sir Good, Sir Kay, and two squires named Alt and Maj were on a dangerous mission. It became desirable that each of the five should assume the guise of one of the other four. As you can imagine, this was readily accomplished by the clever Merlin, and in such a way that no two of the five assumed the guise of the same person.

Arthur's task was to figure out the name of the person each of the five was disguised as. The clues that follow are sufficient.

1. Sir Good assumed the guise of the person who was disguised as Alt.
2. The person who assumed the guise of Sir Kay was portrayed by Merlin.
3. Alt assumed the guise of the person who was disguised as Merlin.

*Solving suggestions on pages 43–49*
*Answers on pages 51–60*

# 8. THE JOUSTING RANKINGS

In this very challenging puzzle, Merlin gave Arthur a list of ten knights as follows, telling the young king that the list represented the rankings of the ten best jousters for the preceding year, #1 being the leading jouster, etc.

1. Good
2. Balter
3. Pure
4. Chaste
5. Grand
6. Black
7. White
8. Brave
9. Glory
10. Noble

"The rankings are different this year," said Merlin. "While the new list consists of the same ten knights as last year's list, none of the ten occupies the same position that he held the year before."

Arthur's challenge was to figure out this year's rankings of the ten knights. The following facts were made known to him:

1. The product of Sir Pure's ranking this year and his ranking last year is the same as the product of Sir Black's ranking this year and his ranking last year. Also, Sir Black's new ranking remains an even number.
2. The sum of Sir Chaste's ranking this year and his ranking last year is the same as the sum of Sir Glory's ranking this year and his ranking last year. Also, Sir Chaste's new ranking remains an even number.
3. The remaining six knights consisted of the following:
   (a) two who were consecutively ranked last year and remain so this year, having switched places in the rankings;
   (b) a third knight, who moved up one position;
   (c) a fourth knight, who moved down one position;
   (d) a fifth knight, who went from an odd-numbered position to an even-numbered one;
   (e) a sixth knight who went from an odd-numbered position to a different odd-numbered position.
4. Sir Grand did not move to the #10 spot in this year's rankings.

*Solving suggestions on pages 43–49*
*Answers on pages 51–60*

# 9. THE PAVILIONS OF THE CHAMPIONS

The magnificent pavilions of the five knights judged to be the best jousters in Camelot were set up in a perfect circle on an elevated platform north of the field where on the morrow they would be obliged to meet the challenges of any and all knights who dared to brave their lances. (See the diagram that follows).

Before each pavilion, the emblem of the knight was exhibited on his shield, hung for all to see, and beside each pavilion stood the squire selected to serve the knight during the tournament. Merlin's challenge to Arthur was to determine the name of the knight at each pavilion, that knight's emblem, and the name of the squire serving him on this occasion. The information given was as follows:

The Knights: Sir Brave, Sir Chaste, Sir Good, Sir Pure, Sir White

The shield emblems: bear, dragon, oak tree, falcon, lion

The squires: Altur, Bran, Col, Fel, Hab

1. The pavilion of Col's knight was farther south than Sir Brave's.
2. Sir Brave's emblem was not the oak tree.
3. The pavilion marked "C" was the one where the knight's emblem was the bear.
4. Sir White's pavilion was east of only the pavilion where Altur was the squire and south of only the pavilion where the knight's emblem was the oak tree.
5. The pavilion of the knight served by Fel was west of only the pavilion where Bran was the squire and was not the pavilion where the emblem was the oak tree.
6. Sir Pure's pavilion was between that of the knight served by Bran and that of the knight whose emblem was a falcon.
7. The lion was not the emblem of Fel's knight.
8. Sir Good's pavilion was further north than that of the knight whose emblem was the dragon.
9. The pavilion of the knight whose emblem was the falcon was directly across from Sir Chaste's pavilion.

*Solving suggestions on pages 43–49*
*Answers on pages 51–60*

# 10. DEEDS OF DERRING-DO

In the days before Arthur's reign, the land that was to become Camelot was on one occasion under the threat of a fire-breathing dragon that destroyed everything in its path, of a monstrous man-eating giant, of an evil knight who slew two of the bravest and noblest knights of the land, and of a Saxon spy who was cleverly gathering intelligence information for his own people.

Merlin chose four good and brave knights and said to them, "Go forth and find and slay these forces of destruction and evil. You will be protected by my powers."

The four knights, who were, in alphabetical order, Sir Bountiful, Sir Chivalrous, Sir Daring, and Sir Gallant, set off. One went to the north, one to the south, one to the east, and one to the west, each to slay one of the dreadful beings. Each took with him a favorite squire—they were Alain, Damon, Frey, and Golan. Arthur's task was to determine the nature of each knight's deed, his squire's name, the relative location of his foe, and also to deduce the order in which the four deeds were done. The following information was given:

1. It was not Sir Chivalrous who slew the dragon.
2. The knight served by Frey, who was not Sir Bountiful, slew the giant; this was the first of the four deeds.

3. The deed of Sir Bountiful and that accomplished in a spot east of the future Camelot were consecutive deeds in one or the other order, and both were accomplished before Alain's knight went on his mission to kill the evil knight.
4. The deed of Sir Chivalrous, who was served by Golan, was the second of the four to be accomplished.
5. Damon's knight accomplished his deed in the north.
6. Sir Gallant's deed preceded that of the knight who met his challenge west of the future Camelot.

*Solving suggestions on pages 43–49*
*Answers on pages 51–60*

# SOLVING SUGGESTIONS

**1. The New Year's Eve Ball.** Make a chart with rows and columns and enter into it the facts from clue 1 to obtain the following, in which one line is used for each knight.

| Knights | Order of Arrival | Color |
|---|---|---|
| Pious | | |
| | 2nd | |
| | | white |
| Pure | | |

Use the other clues to finish filling in the chart.

**2. Who Won the Jousting Tournament?** Keep in mind that every time there was a contest there was a winner and a loser. Try to determine which knights definitely won no contests and which did win one or more contests. Clues 2, 3, and 4, will determine the numbers of the three knights who, by clue 1, won one or more contests. Then use the rules by which the tournament was conducted to determine the opponents in each contest and the results of their meeting. (Special hint: from clue 3, #8 must not have won any bouts.)

**3. Name the Knights.** Make a list of the numbers of the knights—#1 through #10, leaving a line for each number—and fill in the names as you determine them. Certain clues will tell you the names of the three knights who won a contest—actually we know one of them won two contests, a second won three, and the third won four. So you can begin by writing their names down on lines 1, 5, and 7. When you determine which one of the three names belongs on each line, cross out the other two names. (Special hint: clue 3 is a key clue.)

**4. The Rankings of the Squires.** Make a chart as follows:

| | Black | Good | Pure | Noble | Wise | Total |
|---|---|---|---|---|---|---|
| Gort | | | | | | |
| Harl | | | | | | |
| Jol | | | | | | |
| Kal | | | | | | |
| Lok | | | | | | |

Fill in all scores given directly in the clues, such as the scores of 5 given to Jol by Sir Black and Sir Good. As you determine other scores enter them into the chart. Remember that in each column you should end up with one each of the numbers 1, 2, 3, 4, and 5.

**5. Mixed-Up Mugs.** Make a chart with 3 columns as follows, filling it in with the information from clues 4 and 5, and completing the column labelled "User" with the remaining names:

| | Mug | Owner | User |
|---|---|---|---|
| 1. | | Hap | Arn |
| 2. | X | | Gar |
| 3. | | | Pel |
| 4. | | | Tul |
| 5. | | | Hap |

**6. Romance Among the Squires and Maids.** Make a diagram as follows:

Mary loved __________, who loved __________, who loved
(1) (2) (3)
__________, who loved __________, who loved __________, who
(4) (5) (6)
loved __________, who loved __________, who loved Mary.
(7) (8)

Above the number 2, put the name of the squire Mary loved; above the number 3, put the name of the maid that this squire loved; above the number 8, the name of the squire who loved Mary, and so forth.

**7. Merlin and the Disguises.** Make a chart and put in it the information from clues 1 and 3 as follows:

| | Person's Name | Person's Disguise |
|---|---|---|
| 1. | Sir Good | Person who was disguised as Alt |
| 2. | Person who was disguised as Alt | Alt |
| 3. | Alt | Person who was disguised as Merlin |
| 4. | Person who was disguised as Merlin | Merlin |
| 5. | | |

First determine who was disguised as Merlin. By clue 3 that person wasn't Alt. Assume it was Sir Good. Do you find a contradiction? Assume it was Sir Kay. Do you find a contradiction?

**8. The Jousting Rankings.** To solve this puzzle it will be helpful to make out a chart as follows:

| | Last Year | This Year |
|---|---|---|
| 1. | Good | |
| 2. | Balter | |
| 3. | Pure | |
| 4. | Chaste | |
| 5. | Grand | |
| 6. | Black | |
| 7. | White | |
| 8. | Brave | |
| 9. | Glory | |
| 10. | Noble | |

As you proceed to solve the puzzle, you will be trying out a number of different possibilities.

**9. The Pavilions of the Champions.** Make a chart as follows:

| | Knight's Name | Emblem | Squire's Name |
|---|---|---|---|
| A | | | |
| B | | | |
| C | | | |
| D | | | |
| E | | | |

Begin with clue 3, and then use clue 4. Fill in the chart as you solve the puzzle.

**10. Deeds of Derring-Do.** Make a chart with a line for each knight and fill in the information as you solve the puzzle. Beginning with clue 4, you obtain the following:

| Knight's Name | Deed | Squire's Name | Location | Order |
|---|---|---|---|---|
| Bountiful | | | | |
| Chivalrous | | Golan | | 2nd |
| Daring | | | | |
| Gallant | | | | |

Special hint: Clues 4 and 3 together identify Sir Chivalrous, Alain's knight, and Sir Bountiful as three separate knights and tell you the location of Sir Chivalrous's deed.

# ANSWERS

**1. The New Year's Eve Ball.** First: Sir Good, white; second: Sir Venerable, blue; third: Sir Pure, gold; fourth: Sir Pious, purple. By clue 1, the four knights were Sir Pious, the knight who arrived second, the knight whose horse wore white trappings, and Sir Pure. These facts may be entered into a chart:

| Knights | Order of Arrival | Color |
|---|---|---|
| Pious | | |
| | 2nd | |
| | | white |
| Pure | | |

Sir Venerable's steed did not wear white trappings (clue 3), so Sir Venerable must be the knight who arrived second. Thus, Sir Good rode the horse with white trappings. We now have:

| Knights | Order of Arrival | Color |
|---|---|---|
| Pious | | |
| Venerable | 2nd | |
| Good | | white |
| Pure | | |

By clue 2, Sir Pious arrived fourth. Sir Good did not arrive third (clue 4), so he arrived first, and the horse with blue trappings was Sir Venerable's mount (also clue 4). Sir Pure arrived third (process of elimination). By clue 5, the horse with purple trappings wasn't ridden by Sir Pure, so it was Sir Pious's mount. Finally, the horse wearing gold trappings carried Sir Pure (process of elimination).

**2. Who Won the Jousting Tournament?** Exactly three knights won one or more contests (clue 1). The first contest was between #1 and # 2, so either #1 or #2 won at least one contest. A second winner was #5, since in order to have contested #6 (clue 2), #5 would have to have defeated a prior opponent. The third winner was #7, since #7 must have defeated #8 in order to have contested #9 (clue 3). By the rules and what we have deduced thus far, we know that #s 3 and 4 won no contests. Both were defeated by the same knight, either #1 or #2. By clue 4, that knight was #1. So #1 defeated #2, #3, and #4 in order. Then, since clue 2 tells us that one contest was between #5 and #6, it follows that #1 lost when he fought #5. So the three winners of one or more matches were #1, #5, and #7. Thus, #5 must have defeated #6, only to have been overcome by #7, who must have gone on to defeat in turn, #s 8, 9, and 10, to win the tournament. In summary, in the order of the matches:

#1 defeated #2, #3, and #4 in succession
#5 defeated #1 and #6 in succession
#7 defeated, in order, #5, #8, #9, and #10

**3. Name the Knights.** #1 is Black; #2 is Pure; #3 is Good; #4 is Glory; #5 is Bad; #6 is Grand; #7 is Noble; #8 is Brave; #9 is Chaste; #10 is White. From the preceding puzzle, we know that #1, #5, and #7 were the three knights who won one or more contests. From clues 1, 2, and 4, these three knights were, in some order, Sir Black, Sir Noble, and Sir Bad. The other seven knights were Sir Pure, Sir Brave, Sir Good, Sir Grand, Sir Chaste and Sir White, and Sir Glory. Sir Good's single contest was four matches before that between Sir Noble and Sir Bad (clue 3). Since both Sir Noble and Sir Bad won one or more contests, they have to have been #5 and #7 in one or the other order. Either way, Sir Good must have been #3, and Sir Black must have been #1 (previous puzzle's solution). Sir Noble defeated Sir Brave in Sir Brave's only contest (clue 2). Suppose Sir Noble had been #5 and Sir Bad #7. Then Sir Brave would have been #6. That would mean two knights whose names begin with "B" had consecutive numbers assigned to them (i.e., Sir Brave would have been #6, and Sir Bad would have been #7), contradicting clue 6. So Sir Noble was #7, Sir Bad was #5, and Sir Brave was *not* #6. Sir Brave was either #8 or #9 (clue 2). He can't have been #9, as then clue 5 couldn't be met. So Sir Brave was #8, whence, by clue 5, we know that Sir Chaste was #9 and Sir White was #10. Sir Bad defeated Sir Grand (clue 4), so, since Sir Grand won no contests, Sir Grand was #6. Sir Glory, then was #4 (clue 7). By elimination, Sir Pure was #2.

**4. The Rankings of the Squires.** The following chart summarizes the solution:

| | Black | Good | Pure | Noble | Wise | Total |
|---|---|---|---|---|---|---|
| Gort | 1 | 2 | 3 | 1 | 1 | 8 |
| Harl | 2 | 1 | 1 | 4 | 2 | 10 |
| Jol | 5 | 5 | 4 | 3 | 5 | 22 |
| Kal | 4 | 3 | 2 | 2 | 3 | 14 |
| Lok | 3 | 4 | 5 | 5 | 4 | 21 |

It is essential to use a chart, as shown on page 44 of the Solving Suggestions. By clue 5, Sir Black and Sir Good gave scores of 5 to Jol. By clue 6, Sir Wise's 2 went to Harl, and Sir Noble's 2 went to Kal. Thus, Harl got a score higher than 2 from Sir Noble. By clue 4, that score was twice Sir Pure's score for Kal; so, Sir Noble gave Harl a 4, and Sir Pure gave Kal a 2. Lok received 21 points in total (clue 8). We now have:

| | Black | Good | Pure | Noble | Wise | Total |
|---|---|---|---|---|---|---|
| Gort | | | | | | |
| Harl | | | | 4 | 2 | |
| Jol | 5 | 5 | | | | |
| Kal | | | 2 | 2 | | |
| Lok | | | | | | 21 |

To have achieved 21 points, Lok must have received one of the following sets of scores: (a) four 5's and one 1; (b) three 5's, one 4, and one 2; (c) three 5's and two 3's; (d) two 5's, two 4's, and one 3; (e) one 5 and four 4's. Since Jol got three scores of 5 (clue 5), we may eliminate (a), (b), and (c). By clue 8, Lok's score from Sir Black was *lower* than any other score he received, so we may eliminate (e). Thus, the true case is (d): Lok received two 5's, two 4's, and one 3. His 5's came from Sir Pure and Sir Noble (clue 7). By clue 8, he received a 3 from Sir Black. Thus, he received scores of 4 from Sir Good and Sir Wise. By clue 3, Kal received a 4 from Sir Black. So Sir Black gave his score of 2 to Harl (clue 1 and process of elimination), whence we may conclude that his score of 1 went to Gort, and Sir Good's score of 1 went to Harl. The chart should now read:

| | Black | Good | Pure | Noble | Wise | Total |
|---|---|---|---|---|---|---|
| Gort | 1 | | | | | |
| Harl | 2 | 1 | | 4 | 2 | |
| Jol | 5 | 5 | | | | |
| Kal | 4 | | 2 | 2 | | |
| Lok | 3 | 4 | 5 | 5 | 4 | 21 |

We now know that Gort is the squire whose highest score was a 3, given by Sir Pure (clue 9). Since Sir Wise gave Harl a 2 and Gort a score lower than 3, he can only have given Gort a score of 1. Jol's third score of 5 came from Sir Wise (process of elimination). So Sir Wise gave Kal a score of 3. Since Sir Noble gave Kal a 2 and Gort a score lower than 3, he gave Gort a 1; by elimination, he gave Jol a score of 3. The score received by Gort from Sir Good is less than 3 and isn't 1, so it must have been 2. By elimination, Sir Good gave his score of 3 to Kal. By clue 2 and elimination, Sir Pure's score of 1 went to Harl, and his score of 4 went to Jol. The winner, then, was Jol with 22 points. Lok was second with 21 points, Kal third with 14, Hal fourth with 10, and Gort fifth with 8.

**5. Mixed-Up Mugs.** The solution is given in the following chart:

| | Mug Marking | Owner | User |
|---|---|---|---|
| 1. | sword | Hap | Arn |
| 2. | X | Pel | Gar |
| 3. | shield | Tul | Pel |
| 4. | horse | Arn | Tul |
| 5. | dragon | Gar | Hap |

By clue 5, the mug painted with an X was used by Gar. A second mug is the one used by Arn, which, by clue 4, belongs to Hap. A third mug is the one Pel used, a fourth is the one Tul used, and the fifth is the one Hap used. The solving chart (see page 45 of Solving Suggestions) should read as follows:

| | Mug Marking | Owner | User |
|---|---|---|---|
| 1. | | Hap | Arn |
| 2. | X | | Gar |
| 3. | | | Pel |
| 4. | | | Tul |
| 5. | | | Hap |

Arn doesn't own the mug marked with an X (clue 5) or the one used by Hap (clue 6), so Arn owns either the mug used by Tul or the mug used by Pel. Suppose the latter were the actual case. Then Pel would own the mug used by Tul (clue 7), so that, by elimination and what we are told in the introduction, Gar would own the mug used by Hap and Tul the one used by Gar. The mug painted with a picture of a horse would be the one owned by Hap (clue 1). The mug with a shield painted on it would be the one owned by Pel (clue 3). Then clue 2 could not be satisfied. We have shown that

Arn owns the mug used by Tul. Tul owns the mug Pel used (clue 7). Gar owns the one Hap used (introduction) and Pel the mug marked with an X, that Gar used (process of elimination). The mug painted with the picture of a horse belongs to Arn (clue 1). Tul owns the mug decorated with the picture of a shield (clue 3). By clue 2, the mug bearing the picture of a dragon is owned by Gar, and the one with the picture of a sword is owned by Hap.

**6. Romance Among the Squires and Maids.** Mary loved Derwent; Derwent loved Fiona; Fiona loved Marc; Marc loved Heloise; Heloise loved Court; Court loved Elise; Elise loved Balder; Balder loved Mary. From what we are told, each maid loved one squire and was loved by one squire, each squire loved one maid and was loved by one maid, and in no case did the object of affection reciprocate the affection. Mary didn't love Balder (clue 1). Mary didn't love Marc (clue 2) or Court (clues 2 and 4). So Mary loved Derwent. Derwent loved the maid who loved Marc (clue 5) and Marc the maid who loved Court (clue 4). So, in the diagram, "Marc" goes above the number 4 and "Court" above the number 6. Therefore, by elimination, Balder loved Mary. By clue 1, Elise loved Balder. Our diagram (see page 46 of Solving Suggestions) appears as follows at this point:

Mary loved Derwent, who loved ________, who loved
(1) (2) (3)
Marc, who loved ________, who loved Court, who loved
(4) (5) (6)
Elise, who loved Balder, who loved Mary.
(7) (8)

Fiona loved the squire who loved Heloise, (clue 3). So Fiona didn't love Court. By elimination, Fiona loved Marc, so "Fiona" goes above the number 3 in the diagram. Thus, Marc loved Heloise (clue 3), and "Heloise" goes above the number 5.

**7. Merlin and the Disguises.** Sir Good was disguised as Sir Kay, Sir Kay as Alt, Alt as Maj, Maj as Merlin, Merlin as Sir Good. We are told that each of the five was disguised as one of the other four, and that no two of the five were disguised as the same person. First, we determine which person was disguised as Merlin. That person was not Alt (clue 3). Suppose he had been Sir Good. Then, by clue 1, Merlin would have been disguised as Alt, so that, by clue 2, Alt would have been disguised as Sir Kay. But this would mean (clue 3) that Sir Kay as well as Sir Good portrayed Merlin. So we have a contradiction of what we are told. By similar reasoning, it was not Sir Kay who portrayed Merlin. For if it had been, then, by clue 3, Alt would have portrayed Sir Kay, so that, by clue 2, Merlin would have been disguised as Alt, whence, by clue 1, Sir Good as well as Sir Kay would have been disguised as Merlin. By elimination, it was the squire Maj who was disguised as Merlin. So Alt was disguised as Maj (clue 3). The person who was disguised as Alt was not Sir Good (clue 1). Suppose that person had been Merlin. Then Alt would have been disguised as Sir Kay as well as Maj (clue 2), a contradiction. So it was Sir Kay who was disguised as Alt. Thus, by clue 1, it was Sir Good who portrayed Sir Kay. By elimination (or by clue 2), Merlin was disguised as Sir Good.

**8. The Jousting Rankings.** This year's rankings are:

| | | | |
|---|---|---|---|
| 1. | Grand | 6. | Good |
| 2. | Black | 7. | Brave |
| 3. | Balter | 8. | White |
| 4. | Pure | 9. | Noble |
| 5. | Glory | 10. | Chaste |

By clue 1, either (a) Pure went from #3 to #4 and Black from #6 to #2, or (b) Pure went from #3 to #8 and Black from #6 to #4. By clue 2, either (c) Chaste moved from #4 to #6 and Glory from #9 to #1, or (d) Chaste went from #4 to #8 and Glory from #9 to #3, or (e) Chaste went from #4 to #10 and Glory from #9 to #5. The possible combinations of (a) and (b) with (c), (d) and (e) are: (a) and (c); (a) and (d); (a) and (e); (b) and (c); (b) and (d); and (b) and (e).

The possibility of both (b) and (d) having occurred may be ruled out at once because that would put Pure and Chaste in the same position this year.

The possibility of both (a) and (d) having occurred, as well as that of (b) and (c) having occurred, are eliminated by clue 3a, since, by that clue, the two knights who switched positions were either #1, Good, and #2, Balter, or #7, White, and #8, Brave.

Let us suppose that (a) and (c) occurred: Pure moved from #3 to #4, Black from #6 to #2, Chaste from #4 to #6, and Glory from #9 to #1. Then the knights who switched positions (clue 3a) would have been White and Brave, while the knights of clues 3b and 3c would have been, respectively, Noble, moving from #10 to #9, and Balter, moving from #2 to #3. Then, Good, #1, would be the knight of clue 3e, moving from #1 to #5. By elimination of any other possibility, Grand would have moved from #5 to #10, but, by clue 4, this cannot have occurred.

Now suppose that both (b) and (e) occurred: Pure went from #3 to #8 and Black from #6 to #4, while Chaste went from #4 to #10 and Glory from #9 to #5. Then the two consecutively-ranked knights who switched positions would have been Good and Balter. To satisfy clue 3b, #7 would have moved to #6 or #8 would have moved to #7 or #10 would have moved to #9. If #7 had moved to #6, clue 3d could not be met. If #8 had moved to #7, then to satisfy clue 3c, #5 would have moved to #6. Then 3d cannot be met. If #10 had moved to #9, then to satisfy clue 3c, #5 would have moved to #6. Again, however, clue 3d cannot be met.

By elimination, the actual solution to clues 1 and 2 is (a) and (e): Pure moved from 3 to 4, Black from 6 to 2, Chaste from 4 to 10, and Glory from 9 to 5. Thus, by clue 3a, #7, Sir White and #8, Sir Brave, switched places in the rankings. Either Sir Good (#1) or Sir Grand (#5) moved to position 6 (clue 3d). In either case, the knight of clue 3c must be Sir Balter (#2 in the original rankings), who moved to position 3. Only Sir Noble can be the knight of clue 3b, moving from #10 to #9. Necessarily, then, since none of the knights retained his original ranking, #1, Good, moved to #6, and #5, Grand, to #1, and clues 3d and 3e are met.

**9. The Pavilions of the Champions.** A: Sir Good, oak tree, Hab; B: Sir Chaste, lion, Bran; C: Sir Pure, bear, Col; D: Sir Brave, falcon, Altur; E: Sir White, dragon, Fel. By clue 3, pavilion C belonged to the knight whose emblem was the bear. By clue 4, Sir White's pavilion was E, Altur was the squire at pavilion D, and the oak tree was the emblem of the knight at pavilion A. Bran was the squire at B (clue 5). By clue 6, the knight at D had the emblem of the falcon. Sir Chaste had pavilion B (clue 9). Sir Brave's pavilion was not C (clue 1) or A (clue 2), so Sir Brave had pavilion D. Col's knight had pavilion C (clue 1). Fel's knight did not have pavilion A (clue 5), so Fel's knight had pavilion E, and Hab's knight, by elimination, had pavilion A. By clue 7, the lion was not Sir White's emblem, so the knight whose emblem is the lion had pavilion B, and the dragon, by elimination, was the emblem of pavilion E's knight. By clue 8, Sir Good's pavilion was A. By elimination, Sir Pure's was C.

**10. Deeds of Derring-Do.** First deed: Sir Gallant, killing giant, Frey, south; 2nd deed: Sir Chivalrous, killing Saxon spy, Golan, east; 3rd deed: Sir Bountiful, slaying dragon, Damon, north; 4th deed: Sir Daring, killing evil knight, Alain, west. By clue 4, the deed of Sir Chivalrous, who was served by Golan, was the second of the four to be accomplished. By clue 3, the deed of Sir Bountiful and that accomplished in a spot east of the future Camelot were consecutive deeds in one or the other order, and both were accomplished before Alain's knight went on his mission to kill the evil knight. So Sir Chivalrous, Alain's knight, and Sir Bountiful are three of the knights. Alain's knight's deed was either the third or last to be accomplished, and Sir Chivalrous's deed was the second of the four to be accomplished. So Sir Chivalrous's deed is one of the two mentioned in clue 3, and can only be the one undertaken east of the future Camelot. By clue 2, Frey's knight, who wasn't Sir Bountiful, accomplished the first deed: killing the giant. So Bountiful's deed was the third of the four, and Alain's knight's deed the last of the four. Sir Bountiful's squire can only have been Damon (process of elimination). By clue 5, Sir Bountiful's deed took place north of the future Camelot. By clue 6, Sir Gallant was served by Frey, and Alain's knight, who, by elimination, was Sir Daring, accomplished his heroic act west of the future Camelot. Sir Gallant's deed was undertaken south of the future Camelot (process of elimination). By clue 1, only Bountiful could have slain the dragon. By elimination, Sir Chivalrous defeated the Saxon spy.

# CHAPTER III MERLIN IS CHALLENGED

## *By Knights, Normals, Spies, and Other Characters*

The kinds of puzzles in this chapter have been popularized among logic puzzle lovers and taken to heights of perfection by that master puzzlemaker, Raymond Smullyan. You may find yourself becoming dizzy if you attempt to solve all these puzzles at one sitting.

To solve these puzzles you will need to use the contradiction method. You make an assumption that some fact is true and then determine whether the assumption leads to a contradiction (of a fact known to be true). In the real world, we use the method of contradiction without even realizing it. For example, if someone tells you, "All dogs are poodles," you know that his statement is untrue because you know of other dogs that are not poodles (collies, for example).

In solving these puzzles, what you must do is:

1. Assume that a particular fact is true;
2. Check the assumption against the facts you have been given, until:
3. You find a contradiction or
4. You are satisfied there is no contradiction

Some of the puzzles in this chapter require an understanding of the concepts of disjunction and conjunction as they are used by logicians. In real life if I say, "I will go on vacation in June or I will go on vacation in July," or, more simply, "I will go on vacation in June or July," you would undoubtedly take my statement to mean that I will go on vacation during either the month of June or the month of July *but not during both those months*. However, if I were fortunate enough to go on vacation both in June and in July, you would undoubtedly still agree that my statement ("I will go on vacation in June or in July") was true. In logic, this inclusive use of "or" is universal. If *P* and *Q* are two statements, then: "*P* is true or *Q* is true," means that at least one, and possibly both, of *P* and *Q* are true.

We also need to agree on what is meant when it is said that the statement "*P* is true or *Q* is true" is a *false* statement. Such a statement is false only when *P* and *Q* are both false. Thus, in the example above, the statement is true only if I fail to go on a vacation during both June and July.

As to conjunction, the statement "*P* is true and *Q* is true," or, more simply "*P* and *Q*," is a true statement only when *P* and *Q* are both true, but is a false statement if either *P* is false or *Q* is false.

## KNIGHTS, NORMALS, AND SPIES

During the time of Arthur, when England was constantly under the threat of invasion, spies were sent into Arthur's land to gather secret information. Let us imagine that a spy always lied, a knight was always truthful, and all others were "normal people" who sometimes told the truth and sometimes lied.

Merlin was always on the alert to identify spies. Here are some of the situations he might have encountered.

# 1. KNIGHT, NORMAL, AND SPY I

Merlin encounters three individuals who are personally unknown to him. We will call them "A," "B," and "C." Merlin knows that each of the three is of a different type: one is a knight, one is a spy, one is a normal. The three make the following statements:

A: C is not a spy.

B: A is not a knight.

C: B is a knight.

Provide a classification of each of the three.

# 2. KNIGHT, NORMAL, AND SPY II

Merlin again encounters three individuals unknown to him. It is known that one is a knight, one a spy, and one a normal.

A: B is a normal and his statement is true.

B: I'm a normal.

C: B is a normal or his statement is false.

Provide a classification of A, B, and C.

# 3. WHICH ONE IS THE KNIGHT?

Once more Merlin encounters three individuals who are unknown to him. Each makes a statement. Merlin knows only that at least one of the three is a knight. Which one is definitely a knight? Can it be determined what the others are?

A: B is a spy.

B: A is a knight.

C: Either A or B is telling the truth.

*Solving suggestions on pages 73–76*
*Answers on pages 77–81*

## 4. THE THREE SUSPECTS

One of Merlin's apprentices reported an incident to him in which three men were tried for being spies. Said the apprentice to Merlin, "The judge knew that at least one of the three was a spy and at least one of the three was a knight."

"What did the three say at their trial?" asked Merlin.

"I don't remember exactly," said the apprentice, "but I do know that, on the basis of what was said, the judge, who is known to be a superb logician, was able to determine that only one of the three was a spy and was able to identify him."

"What *do* you remember about what the suspects said?" asked Merlin impatiently.

"Well, I know that the second suspect said that what the first suspect said was false and that the third suspect said that the first suspect was a spy. I also remember that the first suspect either said he was a normal or said that he was a knight, but I can't remember which."

From this information, Merlin was able to figure out what the first suspect had said and also to determine which suspect was definitely a spy. Can you?

## LIARS AND DAYS OF THE WEEK

In an unusual land visited by Merlin in his travels, some of the inhabitants lie on Mondays, Wednesdays, and Fridays and tell the truth on the other days of the week, while the rest lie on Tuesdays, Thursdays, and Saturdays and tell the truth on the other days of the week.

## 5. WHAT DAY OF THE WEEK IS IT (I)?

A Monday-Wednesday-Friday liar says, "I told the truth yesterday." What day of the week is it?

## 6. WHAT DAY OF THE WEEK IS IT (II)?

In the same strange land, two inhabitants are encountered: one we will call "A," the other "B." A is a Monday-Wednesday-Friday liar. B is a Tuesday-Thursday-Saturday liar. On what day of the week is it possible for A and B to make the following statements:

A: Yesterday was Sunday.

B: Tomorrow is Saturday.

*Solving suggestions on pages 73–76*
*Answers on pages 77–81*

## 7. WHAT DAY OF THE WEEK IS IT (III)?

Two inhabitants of the same land are encountered. It is known that one is a Monday-Wednesday-Friday liar and the other a Tuesday-Thursday-Saturday liar. The two inhabitants make the following statements:

A: Yesterday I told the truth.

B: Yesterday was Monday.

What day of the week is it? Which type of liar is each of the two?

## 8. WHAT DAY OF THE WEEK IS IT? IS IT FAIR OR RAINING?

In a still stranger land, the inhabitants are "truthers" or liars depending not only on the day of the week but also on whether the day is fair or rainy. Three inhabitants are met. It is known that A lies on fair Tuesdays, Thursdays, and Saturdays, and on rainy Mondays, Wednesdays and Fridays. At all other times he tells the truth. On the other hand, both B and C lie on fair Mondays, Wednesdays, and Fridays and on rainy Tuesdays, Thursdays, and Saturdays. At all other times they tell the truth. A, B and C make the following statements:

A: It is raining and today is Tuesday.

B: It is fair or today is Tuesday.

C: It wasn't Wednesday yesterday and it won't be Wednesday tomorrow.

What day of the week is it? It is fair or is it raining?

# THE LAND OF THE GREEN ELVES AND THE STOLEN BAKED GOODS

Merlin was called to the land of the green elves where an epidemic of petty stealing was taking place. It seems that no elf wife dared put her freshly baked goods onto the windowsill to cool without running the risk of some pesky elf making off with her baking.

## 9. WHO PILFERED THE PIES?

In the first case, three elves suspected of stealing two pies were brought before Merlin. It was known that one of the three was innocent and the other two had conspired in the theft. It was also known that of the statements made by the three exactly one was true—not necessarily the statement made by the innocent elf. The elves' statements were as follows:

Arn: I am innocent

Birn: Con is guilty

Con: Birn is guilty

Merlin was able to identify one of the two thieves, but of the other two he was unable to tell who was guilty and who was innocent.

*Solving suggestions on pages 73–76*
*Answers on pages 77–81*

## 10. WHO STOLE THE BREAD?

In the next case, one of the same three elves was known to have pilfered and eaten two loaves of bread all by himself. The three made statements, and it is known that the thief made a false statement. Merlin was able to use this information to identify the thief. The statement made by the three were:

Arn: I stole the bread.

Birn: Arn is not telling the truth.

Con: Birn stole the bread.

## 11. THE MISSING MEAT PASTRIES

In this case, the same three elves were suspects in the case of the missing meat pastries. It was known that exactly one of the three was guilty and that only one of the three made a true statement; it was not known whether the true statement was made by one of the two innocent elves or by the guilty elf. The statements the three made were:

Arn: Either Birn is guilty or Con is guilty.

Birn: I am not guilty.

Con: Arn isn't guilty.

## 12. THE DOUGHNUT RAID

Two elves were known to have been accomplices in the daring raid on two dozen doughnuts. Four suspects were brought in: Arn, Birn, Con, and a fourth elf named Dob. In this case, the suspects' statements are not at issue. What was known was that the following were actual facts:

1. If Arn is guilty, so is Birn.
2. Either Birn or Con, or both, is innocent.
3. If Con is innocent, Dob is guilty.
4. Con and Dob don't get along, hence would not have been accomplices.

*Solving suggestions on pages 73–76*
*Answers on pages 77–81*

# 13. A MASTER ROBBERY

In this final case, the same four elves were suspects in the master robbery of two different windows on the same day. Four pies and two cakes were stolen and presumably eaten by the rascally thieves. The following statements were made by the four. It was known that two statements were true and two false, and that the two thieves are the ones who made the false statements. It was also known that the thieves rode horses in committing the theft. The statements made were as follows:

Arn: Con can ride.

Birn: Either Con is guilty or Dob is innocent.

Con: Dob is guilty.

Dob: Either Con is guilty or Arn is guilty.

*Answers on pages 77–81*

# SOLVING SUGGESTIONS

**1. Knights, Normals, and Spies I.** The long way to do this is to make a chart of all the possible combinations. Then, for each combination, look for any contradiction. If the puzzle has a valid solution, only one combination will satisfy all the given facts. The possible combinations are shown in the following chart:

| | | | | | | |
|---|---|---|---|---|---|---|
| Knight | A | A | B | B | C | C |
| Spy | B | C | A | C | A | B |
| Normal | C | B | C | A | B | A |

**2. Knights, Normals, and Spies II.** See solving suggestions for puzzle 1.

**3. Which Is the Knight?** Start with C's statement.

**4. The Three Suspects.** Consider the four possibilities for A:

A said he was a knight and he was a knight

A said he was a knight and he was not a knight

A said he was a normal and he was a normal

A said he was a normal and he was not a normal

Which one of the above satisfies the given facts.

**5. What Day of the Week Is It (I)?** Make a list of the days of the week. Write down beside each day whether the person lies or tells the truth on that day. Now, on which day could he have said, "I told the truth yesterday."

**6. What Day of the Week Is It (II)?** First, decide whether: (a) both statements are true; (b) both statements are false; or (c) one statement is true and one is false. Now ascertain the one day of the week that satisfies your conclusion.

**7. What Day of the Week Is It (III)?** First, decide on what day or days A could have made his statement if (a) he were a Monday-Wednesday-Friday liar, and (b) he were a Tuesday-Thursday-Saturday liar. Then do the same for B. Figure out on what day both statements could have been made.

**8. What Day of the Week Is It? Is It Fair or Raining?** Prove that either A's statement is true and B's and C's are both false, or A's statement is false and B's and C's are both true. Once you have done this—and figured out which of the two alternatives is the case—you are well on your way to a solution.

**9. Who Pilfered the Pies?** Assume Arn's statement is true. What conclusions does this assumption lead to.

**10. Who Stole the Bread?** Examine each statement and, using what you are told, determine which one of the three can be true.

**11. The Missing Meat Pastries.** Assume Arn's statement is true; what does that tell you about Con's statement?

**12. The Doughnut Raid.** List all the possible pairs of accomplices and use the given facts to eliminate those pairs that could not have made the theft.

**13. A Master Robbery.** First determine whether Arn is one of the two thieves.

# ANSWERS

**1. Knights, Normals, and Spies I.** A is the knight, B is the spy, C is the normal. We know that exactly one of the three is a knight and one a spy. The knight can't be C since, if C were a knight his statement would be a true statement; therefore, B would also be a knight. Now, suppose B is the knight. Then C's statement would be true, so C would not be the spy, exactly what A said. So A's statement would be true also, so none of the three could be a spy, contrary to what we are told. So B is not the knight. So A must be the knight. Now B's statement is false, and as B is not a knight, C's statement is false. But, from A's statement, C is not a spy, so C is the normal, and B is the spy.

**2. Knights, Normals, and Spies II.** A is the normal, B is the spy, C is the knight. A knight would not say that he is a normal, so B cannot be the knight. Nor can B be the normal, for then, B's statement would be true, whence both A's and C's would also be true—a contradiction since at least one of the statements is false (the one made by the spy). So B is the spy, and his statement is false. Thus, A's statement is false, so A is the normal of the three. Finally, C is the knight (the "his statement is false" part of C's statement is true, making the entire statement true).

**3. Which is the Knight?** C is a knight, A is a normal, B is a spy. One of the three is a knight, so C must be telling the truth. If not, then all three individuals are lying, and none could be a knight. Suppose B's statement is true. Then A is a knight. Since knights are always truthful, A's statement would be true: B would be a spy. But that presents us with the contradiction that a spy has made a true statement. So B's statement is untrue. Since C's statement is true, it follows that A's is also. Thus, B is a spy (since A's statement is true) and A is not a knight (since B's statement is false). So A must be a normal. C is, then, the knight.

**4. The Three Suspects.** We show that if A had said that he was a knight, the judge would not have been able to positively identify a spy among the three prisoners. In this case, any one of the three could be a spy. The first prisoner could be a spy and either one of the others could be a knight. The second prisoner could be a spy if the first is a knight and the third a normal (lying on this occasion). The third prisoner could be a spy and either the first or second a knight. So A must have said "I'm a normal." Now if A's statement is true, he is a normal, so both B's and C's statements would be false, and we would be left with no knight among the three. So A's statement must be false; he is not a normal, but he lied, so he must be a spy. So B's and C's statements are both true. The judge could not have known which of B and C was a knight and which was a normal, but, of course, the judge has done his duty by determining that A is the only spy.

**5. What Day of the Week Is It (I)?** Sunday. If it were Tuesday, Thursday, or Saturday, days on which the inhabitant always tells the truth, he would not lie and say he had told the truth on the previous day. If it were Monday, Wednesday, or Friday, days on which he always lies, he would not say he had told the truth on the previous day—for such a statement would be true. It is Sunday, a day on which the inhabitant tells the truth, and the only day of the week on which it is true that he tells the truth on the preceding day.

**6. What Day of the Week Is It (II)?** Friday. Clearly these statements were not made on Sunday, the one day of the week on which all inhabitants tell the truth. On any other day of the week one of the inhabitants tells the truth and the other lies, so one statement must be true and the other false. Suppose A's statement is the true statement; then yesterday was Sunday, and today is Monday. But A lies on Mondays, so this cannot be the case. So A's statement is false. Thus, B's statement is true: tomorrow is Saturday and today is Friday. (B tells the truth on Fridays and A lies on Fridays, so there is no contradiction.)

**7. What Day of the Week Is It (III)?** Monday. From puzzle 5, we know that if A were a Monday-Wednesday-Friday liar, he could make the statement, "I told the truth yesterday," only on a Sunday. However, if A were a Tuesday-Thursday-Saturday liar, he could have made his statement only on Monday. So either:

A is a Mon.-Wed.-Fri. liar and spoke on Sunday

or

A is a Tues.-Thurs.-Sat. liar and spoke on Monday

If B were a Mon.-Wed.-Fri. liar, he could have said, "Yesterday was Monday," on a Monday, a Wednesday, or Friday because the statement would have been a lie on those days. Or, he could have said it on a Tuesday, because the statement would be true on a day when he tells the truth. On the other hand, if B were a Tues.-Thurs.-Sat. liar, he could have made the statement "Yesterday was Monday" only on a Thursday or Saturday, the only days on which it is a fact both that he lies and the statement is a lie. He couldn't have made it on a Monday, Wednesday, or Friday because the statement would be false on a day when he tells the truth. So, either:

B is a Mon.-Wed.-Fri. liar and spoke on Monday, Tuesday, Wednesday, or Friday

or

B is a Tues.-Thurs.-Sat. liar and spoke on Thursday, or Saturday

We seek a day of the week on which both statements could be made, one by one type and the second by the other type of liar. Obviously the only day that could be would be Monday, and only if A is a Tues.-Thurs.-Sat. liar and B a Mon.-Wed.-Fri. liar.

**8. What Day of the Week Is It? Is It Fair or Raining?** It is a clear Saturday. It cannot be a Sunday, clear or rainy, since A tells the truth on Sunday, whereas, "It is raining and today is Tuesday" is only true on a rainy Tuesday. So, since the three statements were made on a day other than Sunday, either A's statement is true (it's a rainy Tuesday) and both B's and C's are false, or A's statement is false and both B's and C's are true. Now A's statement cannot be true, for then B's would also be true (because the "It is Tuesday" portion of it would be true. Therefore, A's statement is false, and both B's and C's are true. Any false statement made by A was made on a fair Tuesday, Thursday, or Saturday, or on a rainy Monday, Wednesday, or Friday. Any true statement made by B was made on a fair Tuesday, Thursday, or Saturday or a rainy Monday, Wednesday, or Friday. But, since B's statement is known to be true as to its content, it could not have been made on a rainy Monday, Wednesday, or Friday. So B's statement was made, and A's statement was made, on a fair Tuesday, Thursday, or Saturday. The only one of those days on which C's statement is true, as it must be, is a clear Saturday (on a clear Tuesday, his statement would be false because tomorrow would be Wednesday, while on a clear Thursday, his statement would be false because the previous day was Wednesday).

**9. Who Pilfered the Pies?** Arn is definitely guilty. Assume Arn's statement is the one of the three that is true. Then Arn is not guilty, so both Birn and Con are guilty. But that means that both Birn's and Con's statements would be true. This is a contradiction of what we are told (i.e., that just one of the three statements is true). So Arn's statment is false. Therefore Arn is guilty. Attempts to discover whether Birn or Con is the other guilty one are unfruitful. If the one true statement were made by Birn, then Con is guilty, and if it were made by Con then Birn is guilty. Since we have no means of determining which of the two made the true statement, we cannot determine whether it is Birn or Con who is the other thief.

**10. Who Stole the Bread?** Con is the thief. If Arn were the thief, his statement would be true, contradicting the fact that the thief lied. So Arn's statement is false, and Arn is not the thief. This means that Birn told the truth when he said that Arn was lying. So Birn is not the thief. By elimination, Con is the thief (and he lied when he identified Birn as the thief).

**11. The Missing Meat Pastries.** Arn is guilty. If Arn's statement is the one that is true, then Arn is innocent (since only one of the three is the thief), so Con's statement is true also. We cannot have two statements true, so Arn's statement is false. Since the content of Arn's statement is false, neither Birn nor Con is guilty and Arn is. The one who made a true statement is Birn.

**12. The Doughnut Raid.** The thieves are Birn and Dob. The two were not Arn and Con, or Arn and Dob (statement 1), or Birn and Cob (statement 2), or Arn and Birn (statement 3), or Con and Dob (statement 4). By elimination, they were Birn and Dob.

**13. A Master Robbery.** The thieves were Birn and Dob. If Arn were one of the thieves, his statement would be false, so Con would be unable to ride and would be innocent. That would mean Con's statement was true; hence, Dob would be guilty. That means Dob's statement would have to be false. But Dob said that *either* Con was guilty *or* Arn was guilty, and, since Arn *is* guilty under our assumption, Dob's statement would be true. From this contradiction, we know that Arn must be innocent. If Birn is also innocent, then both Con and Dob are guilty. But that cannot be true since Con's statement would be true if Dob is innocent (i.e., this is a contradiction since the two thieves lied). So Birn must be guilty; hence Birn's statement is false. That means Con is innocent and Dob is guilty. (Note: this checks out, since both Dob's statement would be untrue and Con's statement would be true.)

# CHAPTER IV
# MORE CHALLENGES FOR ARTHUR

*In Which Arthur Deals with Dragons, Princesses, and Fairies*

## PRINCESSES AND DRAGONS

Arthur happily solved all the logic puzzles described in Chapter II and begged Merlin for more. "That's enough for one day," said Merlin and he waved the boy off impatiently. But not long afterwards, on an afternoon when the young king was bored with his regular studies and tired of practicing with sword and lance, the sorcerer decided it was time for some more tests of Arthur's reasoning abilities. With arms uplifted and hands turned palm upwards, Merlin mumbled a strange-sounding incantation. Arthur was enveloped in a cloud of smoke. When the smoke dissipated, Arthur found himself with Merlin in a deep wooded valley between hills. "All of these hills contain caves," said Merlin. "Some of the caves are empty, but those that are not empty contain either a dragon or a princess. The princesses have been imprisoned by an evil witch. Any you can find will be freed."

## 1. A PRINCESS OR A DRAGON I?

"This is a puzzle I gave a Saxon spy to solve," said Merlin, "with the understanding that if he made the wrong choice he would face the fire of a dragon, whereas the right choice would merely land him in prison."

Arthur found himself trembling as Merlin explained, "Look up the hill before you. You will see two caves. One of the caves contains a princess, and the other contains a fire-breathing dragon. Each cave has a sign above its entrance. One sign is true; the other is false. Which cave would you choose? The Saxon spy was forced to enter the cave he chose."

When Arthur hesitated, Merlin added, "Make the wrong choice, Arthur, and I will save you nonetheless." Arthur breathed a sigh of relief and went on to make the right choice. Can you? The signs read as follows:

| A | B |
|---|---|
| AT LEAST ONE OF THESE TWO CAVES CONTAINS A DRAGON | A DRAGON IS IN THE OTHER CAVE |

## 2. PRINCESS OR DRAGON II?

Arthur found the preceding puzzle to be very easy, and teased Merlin, "My dear Merlin, can you not in your wisdom come up with something harder than that? Surely the Saxon prisoner is in jail and not eaten by a dragon."

"You are correct, Arthur," said Merlin, "and for that reason, I found it necessary with future spies to devise harder tasks." Merlin mumbled some strange words, waved his wand, and Arthur found himself on a hillside facing three caves labelled "A," "B," and "C." Each cave had a sign above its entrance.

"Try your hand at this puzzle," said Merlin. "The facts are these: one of these three caves contains a princess, one contains a dragon, and one is empty. Only the cave containing the princess has a true sign above it. You must figure out the contents of each cave."

Arthur found this puzzle to be much harder than the previous one.

| A | B | C |
|---|---|---|
| CAVE C IS EMPTY | THE DRAGON IS IN THIS CAVE | THE MIDDLE CAVE IS EMPTY |

## 3. A PRINCESS OR DRAGON III?

Merlin mumbled an incantation, waved his wand, and Arthur and he ended up facing two caves on yet another hill. "This puzzle is somewhat different," said Merlin to Arthur. "There are two caves, each with a sign above it. The signs are either both true or both false. You are to determine what each cave contains. Each contains either a princess or a dragon."

The signs read as follows:

| A | B |
|---|---|
| EITHER THIS CAVE CONTAINS A DRAGON OR THE OTHER CAVE CONTAINS A PRINCESS | THE OTHER CAVE CONTAINS A PRINCESS |

*Solving suggestions on pages 95–96*
*Answers on pages 97–100*

# 4. PRINCESS OR DRAGON IV?

Merlin whisked Arthur off by magic to a hill with four caves labelled "A," "B," "C," and "D," as shown in the diagram that follows. "In this last princess or dragon puzzle," said Merlin, "two of the four caves have signs with true statements and the other two have signs with false statements. Each of the two caves with true statements contains a princess, and each of the two with false statements contains a dragon, so that, of course, the two caves with princesses have signs with true statements, and the two caves with dragons have signs with false statements."

The signs on the caves read as follows:

| A | B | C | D |
|---|---|---|---|
| THE CAVE NEXT TO THIS ONE CONTAINS A DRAGON | THE CAVE LABELLED "C" DOES NOT CONTAIN A DRAGON | ONE OF THE CAVES NEXT TO THIS ONE CONTAINS A DRAGON | THE CAVE NEXT TO THIS ONE CONTAINS A DRAGON |

# THE LAND OF PINK AND GREEN FAIRIES

Having successfully solved all the "princess or dragon" puzzles, Arthur was magically transported to the land of pink and green fairies, all of whom are of the feminine sex. Merlin explained to Arthur, "*Real* pink fairies always tell the truth, and *real* green fairies always lie. However, it is within my power to change a pink fairy to a green fairy, or a green fairy to a pink fairy, or both. A pink fairy disguised as a green fairy still always tells the truth, while a green fairy disguised as a pink fairy still always lies."

## 5. CAN A FAIRY SAY "I'M A GREEN FAIRY?"

Arthur's first puzzle was to answer the question: Is it possible in this land of pink and green fairies, for any fairy to say "I'm really a green fairy"?

*Solving suggestions on pages 95–96*
*Answers on pages 97–100*

## 6. PINK OR GREEN FAIRY?

Arthur was introduced to two pink-looking fairies. We will call them "A" and "B." The fairies made the following statements:

A: B is a green fairy.

B: I'm the same kind of fairy as A.

Arthur was to provide a classification of each fairy.

## IMPLICATION (IF-THEN STATEMENTS) IN FORMAL LOGIC

Before a solution of the next puzzle is attempted, another digression into the area of formal logic is required. We need to know what is meant when we say that an if-then statement is true and what is meant when we say that such a statement is false.

Suppose I say, "If I stay home tonight I will watch TV." The "if" part of this statement is the first part "I stay home," and the "then" part is "I will watch TV." Now everyone will agree that *if I stay home and I have made a true statement, then I must watch TV.* Also, everyone will agree that *if I stay home and don't watch TV, I have made a false statement.* But what if I don't stay home? Suppose I visit a friend and we talk. Was my statement "If I stay home I will watch TV" true or false? The not-surprising answer is that, logically speaking, the statement is considered true. Suppose, on the other hand, that I visit a friend and we watch TV together, what then can we say about the truth or falsity of the original statement, "If I stay home I will watch TV"? Again, logically speaking, the statement is true.

In summary, whenever an "if" statement is false, an "if-then" statement is true regardless of whether or not the "then" statement is true. Thus, a statement such as "If horses have two legs, then I'm a monkey's uncle" is said to be a true statement (think of it this way: if horses had two legs maybe I would be a monkey's uncle). If the "if" statement is true, however, then the "if-then" statement is true only if the "then" statement is true.

Now back to the puzzles.

## 7. THREE PINK OR GREEN FAIRIES

Arthur soon realized that the color in which a fairy appears was irrelevant to her true nature. He told this to Merlin with some relish, but the old sorcerer merely replied, "A fairy's appearance is relevant in this next puzzle. Here are three fairies. Each will make a statement. Provide a classification of each fairy and answer the question, 'Does A appear to be a green fairy or a pink fairy?'"

A: B is a pink fairy.

B: If A is a pink fairy, then C is a green fairy.

C: B is a green fairy or A is what she appears to be.

# THE LAND OF YELLOW AND BLUE FAIRIES

In another fairyland, the fairies, all female again, are all either yellow or blue. However, Merlin has changed the fairies' appearances so that all are striped yellow and blue. Each fairy carries a baton which is either a magic wand or an ordinary stick. Whether magic wand or stick, all the batons look the same. Any fairy who is carrying a magic wand always tells the truth, regardless of her true color (blue or yellow), but any fairy carrying an ordinary stick always lies, regardless of her true color.

Merlin, of course, explained all this to Arthur before he transported the young king to this strange land. Then he gave Arthur some more puzzles to solve.

*Solving suggestions on pages 95–96*
*Answers on pages 97–100*

## 8. YELLOW OR BLUE I?

A yellow-and-blue-striped fairy made this statement to Arthur: "Either I am a blue fairy and I have a magic wand, or I am a yellow fairy, and I have an ordinary stick."

Arthur was to determine what kind of fairy she is.

## 9. YELLOW OR BLUE? MAGIC WAND OR NOT?

A yellow-and-blue-striped fairy says, "I am a blue fairy and I am carrying an ordinary stick."

Arthur was asked to decide what kind of fairy she is and to determine whether she is carrying a magic wand or an ordinary stick.

## 10. YELLOW OR BLUE II?

Yet another yellow-and-blue-striped fairy made a statement to Arthur. She said, "If I have a magic wand, I am a yellow fairy."

Arthur was to determine what kind of fairy she is.

## 11. A SECOND "YELLOW OR BLUE, MAGIC WAND OR NOT" PUZZLE

Two yellow-and-blue-striped fairies spoke to Arthur. Merlin explained that one was really a yellow fairy, and the other really a blue fairy. The fairies made the following statements:

A: I am a blue fairy and I am carrying a magic wand.

B: I am a yellow fairy and I am carrying an ordinary stick.

Arthur was to figure out what kind of fairy each is and what kind of baton each carries.

*Solving suggestions on pages 95–96*
*Answers on pages 97–100*

# SOLVING SUGGESTIONS

**1. A Princess or a Dragon I?** No hint; any hint would be a giveaway of the answer.

**2. Princess or Dragon II?** Focus, first, on the sign on the middle cave.

**3. Princess or Dragon III?** Suppose both signs are false. Do you find a contradiction?

**4. Princess or Dragon IV?** Suppose the sign on cave A is true. What conclusions do you reach?

**5. Can a Fairy Say "I'm a Green Fairy"?** No hint; any hint would be a giveaway of the answer.

**6. Pink or Green Fairy?** Assume that A is a real green fairy and look for contradictions.

**7. Three Pink or Green Fairies.** Consider whether it is possible for A and B to be different kinds of fairies.

**8. Yellow or Blue I?** Review the logic of disjunction and conjunction (see pages 63–64) if you are at all confused about this area of logic. Then, suppose the fairy's baton is a magic wand. Does that assumption lead to a conclusion about her type? Finally, suppose her baton is an ordinary stick. Does that assumption lead to a conclusion about her type?

**9. Yellow or Blue? Magic Wand or Not?** What happens if you assume the fairy's baton is magical?

**10. Yellow or Blue II?** The amazing fact that is exemplified in this puzzle is that if Q is a statement, then anytime a fairy says, "If I have a magic wand, then Q," Q must be true whatever Q is. Can you prove this?

**11. A Second "Yellow or Blue Magic Wand or Not" Puzzle.** Show that B must be carrying an ordinary stick. Use this fact to prove what kind of fairy B is. We are told that A is the other kind. Then evaluate A's statement knowing what kind she is.

# ANSWERS

**1. A Princess or a Dragon I?** Cave A does not contain a dragon; cave B does. One of the signs is false and the other true. Since one of the caves contains a dragon, the sign on cave A is necessarily true. Since only one of the signs is true, the one on cave B is false. The dragon, then, is in cave B.

**2. Princess or Dragon II?** The middle cave does not contain a princess, since its sign says it contains a dragon, and the cave containing the princess has a true statement on its sign. Also, if the middle cave contained a dragon, it would not say so, since only the sign on the cave with the princess has a true statement on it. Thus, the middle cave is empty. So, the sign on the middle cave is false. Since the middle cave is empty, the sign on cave C bears a true statement on it. So it contains the princess. The sign above cave A, is, by elimination, false and must contain the dragon.

**3. Princess or Dragon III?** Both caves contains princesses. Suppose both signs bore false statements. Then, by the false statement on cave B, cave A contains a dragon. But that means that the statement on cave A is true, a contradiction. So both signs have true statements on them. By the true statement on cave B, cave A contains a princess. By the true sign on cave A, cave B contains a princess.

**4. A Princess or Dragon IV?** Caves B and C contain the princesses. Suppose the sign on cave A is true, so that cave B contains a dragon. Then the sign on cave B is false (because cave B contains a dragon), and so cave C contains a dragon (because the sign on B, which, under our assumption, is false, says that cave C does not contain a dragon). Then, since cave C contains a dragon, the sign on cave C must be false; but that is a contradiction, since, under our assumption that the statement on cave A is true, cave B contains a dragon. So we have shown that the sign on cave A must be false. Therefore, cave B contains a princess, and therefore it bears a sign with a true statement. Since the statement on cave B is true, it follows that cave C contains a princess and bears a sign with a true statement (which checks out, since, from what we are told, the second dragon must be in cave D; note that the sign on cave D is false, which checks out, since cave C does not contain a dragon).

**5. Can a Fairy Say "I'm a Green Fairy"?** No. If the pink-looking fairy were a real pink fairy, she would tell the truth and would not say that she is a green fairy, and if she were really a green fairy, she would not truthfully say that she was.

**6. Pink or Green Fairy?** A is as she appears to be, a pink fairy; B is really a green fairy. Suppose A is a green fairy. Then A's statement is a lie, so B is a pink fairy. This leads us to the contradiction that B is a pink fairy who has made a false statement. So A must be a pink fairy. Therefore, A's statement that B is a green fairy is true (which checks out without contradiction, since B's statement is false).

**7. Three Pink or Green Fairies.** A and B are pink; C is green; A appears to be green. We show that A and B must be the same kind of fairy (in essence, that is, not necessarily in appearance). Suppose they are two different types. First, suppose A is pink and B is green. This cannot be the case, because if A were a pink fairy, she would not make the false statement that B is pink. Now, suppose A is green and B is pink. This cannot be the case either, because if A were a green fairy, she would not make the true statement that B is pink. So A and B are either both pink fairies or both green fairies. Suppose they are both green. Then A is green, so the "if" part of B's statement ("A is a pink fairy") is false. This means (recalling the discussion of logical implication) that B's statement is true, a contradiction of the assumption that B is a green fairy. So both A and B are pink fairies. Therefore since A *is* a pink fairy and B has made a true "if-then" statement, it follows that C is a green fairy.

Then, remembering what it means for an "or" statement to be false, we know that both parts of C's statement are false (since C is green). Hence, "A is what she appears to be" is a false statement. So A must appear to be green.

**8. Yellow or Blue I?** Blue fairy (it cannot be determined whether she carries a magic wand or an ordinary stick). Suppose the fairy's baton is a magic wand. Then, because she carries a magic wand we know her statement is true, meaning that at least one part is true:

"I am a blue fairy and I have a magic wand" is true

or

"I am a yellow fairy and I have an ordinary stick" is true

The second part is false because we have assumed she is carrying a magic wand. So the first part is true; she is a blue fairy.

Now suppose the fairy is carrying an ordinary stick. Then, because she is carrying an ordinary stick, her statement is false. This means *both* parts of her statement are false: she is not a blue fairy with a magic wand, and she is not a yellow fairy with an ordinary stick. Since she does have an ordinary stick, it is obvious she is not a blue fairy with a magic wand. But since she also is not a "yellow fairy with an ordinary stick," she must be a blue fairy with an ordinary stick, as that is the only way the statement, "I am a yellow fairy and I am carrying an ordinary stick" can be false.

**9. Yellow or Blue, Magic Wand or Not?** Yellow fairy/ ordinary stick. If she were carrying a magic wand her statement would be true, so both parts would be true (The "I am carrying an ordinary stick" part as well as the "I am a blue fairy" part). This can't be the case, so she must be carrying an ordinary stick. Thus, her (compound) statement is false, which means one or the other part of it is false, or both parts are false. We know that the "I am carrying an ordinary stick" part is true, so it must be false that she is a blue fairy; so she is a yellow fairy.

**10. Yellow or Blue II?** Yellow. Suppose that the fairy carries a magic wand. Then the statement, "If I have a magic wand, I am a yellow fairy," must be true (since fairies with magic wands always tell the truth). So the "then" part of her statement would be true: she would be a yellow fairy. Therefore, it is proved that if she carries a magic wand she is a yellow fairy. But that is precisely what she asserted. Therefore, she made a true statement, so she must carry a magic wand. And since we have proved that if she carries a magic wand she is yellow, then it must be true that she is yellow.

**11. A Second "Yellow or Blue, Magic Wand or Not" Puzzle.** A is a yellow fairy carrying an ordinary stick; B is a blue fairy carrying an ordinary stick. B cannot be carrying a magic wand, for if so she would be a "truther," hence wouldn't say she is carrying an ordinary stick. So B is carrying an ordinary stick, which means B always lies. Since it's true that she carries an ordinary stick, the only way she can be lying is if she is a blue fairy. Now consider A. Since the two fairies are of different colors, A is a yellow fairy. Since A is a yellow fairy, her statement that she is a blue fairy carrying a magic wand is false. Then, since she made a false statement, she must be carrying an ordinary stick (since fairies with magic wands do not make false statements). Looking at the analysis with respect to A in another way: knowing that A is a yellow fairy, could a yellow fairy with a magic wand have made the statement A made? Clearly the answer is "No." Hence A has an ordinary stick.

# CHAPTER V
# More Puzzles
*for the Prospective Apprentice*

Merlin decided to challenge a prospective apprentice with a number of new puzzles (although most of the puzzles in this chapter are "math" puzzles, you may be happy to know that many of them can be handily solved without using algebra).

## 1. BOOTS FOR THE OGRES

In a hole in the ogre's lair are three black boots, three brown boots, and three white boots. If the ogre removes one boot at a time without looking at its color, how many must he remove in order to be certain of having pairs of boots in the same color for himself *and* his two ogre-ous sons? (Ogres have two left feet, hence do not need boots for the right foot that are different from boots for the left foot.)

*Solving suggestions on pages 113–115*
*Answers on pages 117–124*

# 2. MONSTER HEADS/ MONSTER FEET

In a land inhabited by monsters, some monsters have two heads each and three feet each, while the remaining monsters have three heads each and four feet each. In all there are 120 heads and 170 feet. How many of each type are there?

# 3. KING ARTHUR MEETS WITH KING BALFOUR

King Arthur and four of his knights met with King Balfour and four of his knights. The ten warriors sat at a round table with Arthur and Balfour directly across from each other, and four knights between them on each side, as diagrammed below. In how many ways could the seats have been occupied by the eight knights if none of Arthur's knights sat next to another of Arthur's knights or to Arthur himself?

# 4. TENDING HORSES

Squires Col and Aken are each in charge of a string of horses. Col takes care of twice as many mares as Aken, who takes care of four times as many stallions as mares, and two more than Col takes care of, which is two more than the number of mares he (Col) takes care of. How many mares and how many stallions does each take care of?

*Solving suggestions on pages 113–115*
*Answers on pages 117–124*

# 5. HOW LONG DID DOB WALK?

Dob, a stonecutter, comes home from work each day by ferry. His wife, Alicia, leaves their cottage at the same time each day to make the trip by mule cart to the ferry dock, meeting Dob at the same time each day. One day Dob finished work before the usual time and took an earlier ferry, arriving one hour earlier than usual at the dock. Not wanting to stand about idly for an hour, he immediately

began walking towards his cottage. Not knowing that Dob had arrived early at the dock, Alicia set out at her usual time and drove at the same speed as usual. On the way to the ferry dock, she met Dob and picked him up. They arrived at their cottage ten minutes earlier than usual. How long did Dob walk (assume a constant rate of speed for Alicia).

## 6. MAGICAL SUBSTANCE

Merlin showed his apprentice a bowl full of some gray looking matter. "This is magical matter," said Merlin. "If I put a 'dash' of it into an empty bowl, it will double its amount each day and completely fill the bowl in four days. How full is the bowl (what fraction of it is full) at the end of the first day?

## 7. CROSSING THE RIVER

Sir Good and Sir Pure need to cross a river with an ogre, a goose, and a bag of corn. Available to them is a small rowboat which will hold two people, or one person plus either the ogre, the goose, or the bag of corn. The problem lies in the facts that: a knight must always be present to keep the goose from eating the corn; a knight must always be present to keep the ogre from eating the goose; Sir Good is afraid of the ogre and won't be in that monster's presence unless Sir Pure is also present. Only the knights can row. How can everyone and everything get across the river?

*Solving suggestions on pages 113–115*
*Answers on pages 117–124*

The balance of this chapter is devoted to math puzzles, all of which can be solved by using logical thinking; no formal mathematical ability is required.

## 8. ADD IT.

What number do each of A, O, and H stand for if each represents a different one-digit number, and:

$$\begin{array}{r} OOO \\ +AAA \\ \hline OOOH \end{array}$$

## THE GAME OF ORDERLY ARRANGEMENTS

In puzzles 9–13 the answer is a series of five different one-digit numbers, between 1 and 9 inclusive, in order from left to right. Each of the series shown represents a player's attempts to duplicate the arrangement, while the X's and O's represent the score given to that attempt. An X means one of the numbers in the player's arrangement appears in the answer in the same position as in the player's arrangement; an O means one of the numbers in the player's arrangement appears in the answer, but its position in the answer is different from its position in the player's arrangement. (Example: suppose the actual arrangement were 12345, and a player suggested the arrangement 62781; the player's arrangement would be scored XO; the player would receive an X for the 2 and an O for the 1).

## 9. ORDERLY ARRANGEMENTS #1

| | | | | | |
|---|---|---|---|---|---|
| (a) | 2 | 4 | 6 | 9 | X |
| (b) | 1 | 3 | 8 | 7 | OO |
| (c) | 4 | 6 | 7 | 8 | X |
| (d) | 2 | 4 | 9 | 3 | OO |

## 10. ORDERLY ARRANGEMENTS #2

| | | | | | |
|---|---|---|---|---|---|
| (a) | 6 | 8 | 1 | 3 | XX |
| (b) | 2 | 4 | 1 | 7 | OO |
| (c) | 8 | 5 | 9 | 2 | XO |
| (d) | 1 | 3 | 4 | 5 | X |

## 11. ORDERLY ARRANGEMENTS #3

| | | | | | |
|---|---|---|---|---|---|
| (a) | 2 | 8 | 6 | 5 | X |
| (b) | 3 | 4 | 6 | 1 | X |
| (c) | 4 | 2 | 7 | 3 | X |
| (d) | 2 | 7 | 9 | 8 | OOO |

## 12. ORDERLY ARRANGEMENTS #4

| | | | | | |
|---|---|---|---|---|---|
| (a) | 5 | 4 | 6 | 2 | X |
| (b) | 4 | 9 | 8 | 6 | X |
| (c) | 6 | 8 | 3 | 7 | X |
| (d) | 2 | 5 | 4 | 1 | XO |

## 13. ORDERLY ARRANGEMENTS #5

| | | | | | |
|---|---|---|---|---|---|
| (a) | 1 | 2 | 3 | 4 | XO |
| (b) | 5 | 6 | 1 | 2 | OO |
| (c) | 7 | 5 | 8 | 9 | XX |
| (d) | 3 | 8 | 9 | 4 | O |
| (e) | 7 | 2 | 8 | 1 | XX |

*Solving suggestions on pages 113–115*
*Answers on pages 117–124*

# PERPLEXING SQUARES

Perplexing squares are little logic problems involving the digits 1, 2, 3, 4, 5, 6, 7, 8, and 9. In each puzzle each of the nine letters stands for a different one of these digits. The objective is to use the clues to determine what digit each letter stands for.

# 14. PERPLEXING SQUARE #1

| | | |
|---|---|---|
| R | S | T |
| U | V | W |
| X | Y | Z |

1. Y is larger than Z, and the sum of Y and Z is 10.
2. $R = U \times U$.
3. The two-digit number obtained when W is multiplied by itself has W as its rightmost digit.
4. $V + 1 = W$; $W + 1 = S$. V is an even number.
5. $X = 7$.

# 15. PERPLEXING SQUARE #2

| | | |
|---|---|---|
| G | H | J |
| K | L | M |
| N | O | P |

1. $O + 2 = J$.
2. In one column of three numbers, reading top to bottom the middle number is twice the top number, and the bottom number is twice the middle number.
3. $P = 2 \times L$.
4. $K + L + M = 12$.

## 16. PERPLEXING SQUARE #3

| | | |
|---|---|---|
| K | L | M |
| N | O | P |
| Q | R | S |

1. The five odd digits are K, L, N, Q, and S.
2. Either one row consists of three consecutive numbers in *descending* order reading left to right, or one column consists of three consecutive numbers in *descending* order reading top to bottom.
3. $M + 2 = P$; $P - 1 = N$;
4. $Q \times R = M$.
5. L is a prime number; that is, L is greater than 1, and is evenly divisible only by itself and the number 1.

## 17. PERPLEXING SQUARE #4

| | | |
|---|---|---|
| A | B | C |
| D | E | F |
| G | H | J |

1. The two-digit number which has D as its leftmost digit and E as its rightmost digit is evenly divisible by C, D, E, F, and H. D is not 1.
2. $H = 3$, and the product of H and J is a two-digit number whose leftmost digit is D, and whose rightmost digit is G.
3. $F + 2 = C$.
4. $B + 2 = G$.

*Solving suggestions on pages 113–115*
*Answers on pages 117–124*

# SOLVING SUGGESTIONS

**1. Boots for the Ogres.** What if the first three boots the ogre removes were three different colors?

**2. Monster Heads/Monster Feet.** I'm afraid this requires algebra, or a lot of trial-and-error.

**3. King Arthur Meets with King Balfour.** Choose the knight for seat #2 first. In how many ways may he be chosen? Now choose the knight for seat #3. He can be chosen in exactly the same number of ways as the knight for seat #2. Once you get to seat #3 you have a more limited number of ways of selecting the knight. How many are left to choose from? Continue from here.

**4. Tending Horses.** This is another puzzle which requires algebra. You will have four equations in four "unknowns."

**5. How Long Did Dob Walk?** Hint: since Alicia and Dob arrived home ten minutes earlier than usual, Alicia drove for ten minutes less than usual. If you cannot come up with a general solution, try doing it by example. For example, you might suppose that Alicia's round trip (cottage to dock) is 60 minutes.

**6. Magical Substance.** When will the bowl be half full? Work backwards from this point.

**7. Crossing the River.** One of the knights must make the first trip. Who can be left alone with whom or what on this first trip?

**8. Add It.** First, determine what O is.

**9. Orderly Arrangements #1.** First, determine that a 5 is needed. Compare the scoring for (a) and (d) to determine which, if either, of 2 and 4 is needed.

**10. Orderly Arrangements #2.** Start by comparing the scoring for (a) with that of (b), and then with that of (d). Doing this will identify two numbers that do not appear in the answer and two that do.

**11. Orderly Arrangements #3.** A good start is to compare the scores for (a) and (d) to identify a number that does not appear in the answer and more than one that does.

**12. Orderly Arrangements #4.** Begin by comparing the scores for (a) and (b) to determine a digit that does not appear in the answer. Compare the scoring for (b) and (c) to identify two other digits that are not needed.

**13. Orderly Arrangements #5.** Begin by using the scoring for (a), (b), and (d) to determine that either 1 or 2 or both is needed. Then, with the help of the scoring for (d) figure out whether just one or both of 1 and 2 is needed.

**14. Perplexing Square #1.** Begin by determining whether W is an even or odd number; then use clues 3, 4, 1 and 5 in that order.

**15. Perplexing Square #2.** Begin by using clues 2 and 3 to determine which of the three columns is the one described in clue 2.

**16. Perplexing Square #3.** Use clue 1 and the fact that, between 1 and 9 inclusive, there are five odd whole digits and four even ones, to identify the even digits. Next use clue 2 and determine which row is referred to in that clue.

**17. Perplexing Square #4.** Begin by using clue 2. Determine what the possibilities are for the leftmost digit of $H \times J$.

# ANSWERS

**1. Boots for the Ogres.** Eight. If the first three boots removed from the chest happened to be three different colors, then a fourth boot must be removed to obtain the first pair of boots of the same color. Assume this is the case, and assume, without loss of generality, that the fourth boot is black. The boots removed at this point would be: one white boot, one brown boot, one pair (two) black boots. Then, suppose that the fifth boot is black, which could be the case, since there are three boots of each color in the chest. Thus, the first five boots removed from the chest would consist of: one white boot, one brown boot, three black boots. So a sixth boot would have to be removed in order to guarantee a second pair. Since the three black boots have all been removed, the sixth boot would have to be either white or brown. Without loss of generality, assume it is brown. So the boots removed to this point would consist of: 3 black boots, 2 brown boots, one white boot. Then, if the seventh boot happened to be brown, the boots removed at this point would be: 3 black boots, 3 brown boots, one white boot. Thus, an eighth boot would have to be removed in order to obtain a third pair of matching boots—which, of course, under our without-loss-of-generality assumptions, would be white.

**2. Monster Heads/Monster Feet.** 30 of the monsters with two heads and three feet each, 20 of the others. This puzzle is most easily solved by using algebra. If $x$ = the number of monsters with two heads and three feet each, and $y$ = the number of monsters with three heads and four feet each, then, from the given facts, we have:

$$(1)\ 2x + 3y = 120$$
$$(2)\ 3x + 4y = 170$$

Now multiply each member of the first equation by 3 and each member of the second by $-2$ and add together the resulting equivalent equations, as follows, to obtain $y = 20$:

$$\begin{array}{lrcr} (1a) & 6x + 9y & = & 360 \\ (2a) & -6x - 8y & = & -340 \\ \hline & y & = & 20 \end{array}$$

Since $y = 20$, we have, from the original equation 1, $2x + 3(20) = 120$, $2x + 60 = 120$, $2x = 60$, $x = 30$.

**3. King Arthur Meets with King Balfour.** 576 ways. Without loss of generality, choose the knight for seat #2 first. From what we are told, he must be a knight of King Balfour. He can be chosen in four different ways. Next, choose the knight for seat #3. He is a knight of King Arthur, and he too can be chosen in four different ways. Then, seat #4 can be filled in three ways, from among Balfour's remaining three knights, and seat #5 in three ways, from among Arthur's remaining three knights. Similarly, seats 7 and 8 can be filled in two ways each, and seats 9 and 10 in two ways each. So the required computation is: $4 \times 4 \times 3 \times 3 \times 2 \times 2 \times 1 \times 1$, which equals 576.

**4. Tending Horses.** This puzzle can best be solved by using algebra. If we let $a =$ the number of mares Aken tends, $b =$ the number of mares Col tends, $c =$ the number of stallions Aken tends, and $d =$ the number of stallions Col tends, we obtain four equations in four unknowns:

$$\begin{array}{ll} (1) & b = 2a \\ (2) & c = 4a \\ (3) & c = d + 2 \\ (4) & d = b + 2 \end{array}$$

Using the fact that $b = 2a$ (equation 1), by substitution of 2a for b in equation 4, we obtain:

$$(5) \qquad d = 2a + 2$$

From equation 2, $c = 4a$, so substituting 4a for c in equation 3, we obtain:

$$(6) \qquad 4a = d + 2$$

Equation 6 may also be written:

$$(7) \qquad d = 4a - 2.$$

Then, by substitution, using equations 5 and 7, we obtain: $2a + 2 = 4a - 2$. Then, by arithmetic, $2a = 4$, so $a = 2$. The rest is obtained by substitution. Since $a = 2$, $b = 4$ (equation 1). Since $a = 2$, $c = 8$ (equation 2). Since $b = 4$, $d = 6$ (equation 4).

**5. How Long Did Dob Walk?** 55 minutes. Since Alicia and Dob arrived home ten minutes earlier than usual, Alicia drove ten minutes less than usual. So she drove one way—towards the ferry dock—for five minutes less than usual. Had she driven for the other five minutes, she would have arrived at the ferry dock at the usual time, one hour later than Dob's actual time of arrival on this particular day. So Dob must have walked for 55 minutes. If you don't understand this, don't be dismayed. It is not an easy problem. Let's look at an example, just to convince you that 55 minutes is the correct answer. Suppose that the time required for one round trip for Alicia is 60 minutes (30 minutes each way). Also, without loss of generality, suppose that she usually leaves the cottage at 6:00, thus arriving at the ferry dock at 6:30 and arriving back home with Dob at 7:00. On the day in question, she leaves at her usual time, 6:00 but she and Dob arrive home at 6:50. Dob arrived at the ferry dock at 5:30 and began walking. Alicia's total round-trip time is 50 minutes, so she drove the mule for 25 minutes before she met Dob. She left home at 6:00 and met Dob at 6:25. Dob had been walking since 5:30, a total of 55 minutes. Try this with a different set of assumptions and you will still arrive at 55 minutes for an answer.

**6. Magical Substance.** $\frac{1}{8}$ full. At the end of the third day the bowl is half full (since it doubles its volume each day and is completely full at the end of the fourth day). So at the end of the second day it is $\frac{1}{4}$ full (since $2 \times \frac{1}{4} = \frac{1}{2}$ at the end of the third day). Thus, at the end of the first day it is $\frac{1}{8}$ full (since $2 \times \frac{1}{8} = \frac{1}{4}$ at the end of the second day).

**7. Crossing the River.** Sir Good rows the corn over, leaves it, and rows back alone. Then Sir Pure rows the ogre over, leaves the ogre with the corn, and rows back alone. Sir Good and Sir Pure then row over together (leaving the goose behind). Sir Pure stays with the corn and the ogre. Sir Good rows back, picks up the goose, and rows across the river.

**8. Add It.** $111 + 999 = 1110$; $O = 1$; $A = 9$; $H = 0$. From the leftmost digit of the answer, O can only be 1. So $A + O$, with 1 "carried," must be 11. Thus, $O + A = 10$. So $A = 9$ and $H = 0$.

**9. Orderly Arrangements #1.** 3 5 7 9. From the scoring of (a) and (b), a 5 is needed, since (a) and (b) together include all possible digits except 5, and together received three marks. Since (a) received one mark of X, and (d) received no X marks, and since 2 and 4 both appear in the same positions in both (a) and (d), we may conclude that neither a 2 nor a 4 is needed. Hence, the scoring of (d) indicates that both 3 and 9 are needed, so, from (a) we may conclude that the answer does not include a 6, and that 9 appears in the answers as the rightmost digit. Since 9 belongs in the rightmost position, the scoring of (c) tells us we do not require an 8. Then, knowing we don't need either a 4 or a 6, the scoring of (c) indicates that we do require a 7, and it belongs in the position second from the right. Next, since one of the O marks for (b) comes from thc 3, it must appear in in the answer as the leftmost digit. By elimination, 5 is the digit second from the left. The answer, then, is 3 5 7 9.

**10. Orderly Arrangements #2.** 6 8 4 2. The two numbers in (a) that are needed are in their correct positions, so, by the scoring for (b), 1 is not needed, and by (d) 3 is not needed. Thus, we need 6 and 8 and they occupy the leftmost and second-from-the-left positions respectively. From the scoring of (b), we need two from 2, 4, and 7: either 2 and 4 or 2 and 7 or 4 and 7. From the scores given (a) and (b), the four numbers are 6, 8, 4, 2 or 6, 8, 2, 7 or 6, 8, 4, 7. So we do not need either 5 or 9. From (c)'s score, then, we need a 2, and it belongs in the rightmost position. From the scoring of (d), we need a 4, and it belongs in the position second from the right. So the answer is 6 8 4 2.

**11. Orderly Arrangements #3.** 9 8 7 1. The digit 2 occupies the same position in (a) as in (d), so, since (a) was scored X and (d) was scored 0 0 0, we do not need a 2. Therefore, by the scoring of (d), we need 7, 9, and 8. Then, from the scoring of (a), we need neither 5 nor 6. To these we can add 3 and 4, from the scoring of (c). By elimination, then, the other needed digit is 1. From the scoring of (a), (b), and (c), the 8 appears in the position second from the left, the 7 to its right, and the 1 in the rightmost position. So the answer is 9 8 7 1.

**12. Orderly Arrangements #4.** 5 9 3 1. By the scoring of (a) and (b), we do not need a 4, for if we did, it would be in the second-from-the-left position, by the scoring for (a), and would have received an 0 score from its position in (b). By the same logic, we don't need a 6 or an 8 (from the scoring of (b) and (c)). Thus, by the scoring of (b), we need a 9 in the second-from-the-left position. From the scoring of (a), we need either a 2 or a 5, and, whichever it is, it is in the correct position in (a). So, from the scoring of (d), we need a 1 in the rightmost position. So from the scoring of (a), we need a 5 rather than a 2 and it goes in the leftmost position. Finally, from the scoring of (c), a 3 goes in the position second from the right.

**13. Orderly Arrangements #5.** 7 5 3 1. If we needed neither 1 nor 2, the scoring of (a) and (b) would indicate that we needed 3, 4, 5, and 6; but that would contradict the scoring for (c). So we need either 1 or 2 or both. If we needed both 1 and 2, we wouldn't need 3, 4, 5, or 6 (from the scoring of (a) and (b)). So we would need two of the digits 7, 8, 9; but this contradicts the scoring of (e). So we need:

1 or 2, but not both

3 or 4, but not both

5 or 6, but not both

Thus, by elimination, we need one of the digits 7, 8, 9. From (e)'s score, we do not need a 9; we need either 7 or 8. Thus, from (c)'s score we need a 5 in the second-from-the-left position. So, from (e)'s score, we do not need a 2 and must need a 1, which, from (e)'s score, belongs in the rightmost position. The X score given (a) was given for either the 3 or the 4; by (d)'s score, it was not given for the 4, so was awarded for the 3. Then, from the scoring of (e), we need a 7 and it goes in the leftmost position.

**14. Perplexing Square #1.** $R = 9$, $S = 6$, $T = 1$, $U = 3$, $V = 4$, $W = 5$, $X = 7$, $Y = 8$, $Z = 2$. W is an odd number, since, by clue 4, $V + 1 = W$, and V is an even number. So, by clue 3, $W = 5$. By clue 4, then, $V = 4$ and $S = 6$. By elimination and clue 2, $U = 3$ and $R = 9$. By clue 1 and elimination, $Z = 2$ and $Y = 8$. By clue 5, $X = 7$. So, by elimination, $T = 1$.

**15. Perplexing Square #2.** $G = 2$, $H = 1$, $J = 9$, $K = 4$, $L = 3$, $M = 5$, $N = 8$, $O = 7$, $P = 6$. By clue 2, in one column of three numbers read from top to bottom, the middle number is twice the top number, and the bottom number is twice the middle number. With P being twice L (clue 3), this column can be neither the middle nor rightmost column; it must be the leftmost column (the one containing G, K, and N). Either $G = 1$, $K = 2$, $N = 4$, or $G = 2$, $K = 4$, $N = 8$. In either case, by clue 3 and elimination, $L = 3$, $P = 6$. If G were 1, K were 2, and N were 4, then M would be 7 (clue 4); clue 1 could not be satisfied if this were the case. So $G = 2$, $K = 4$, $N = 8$. By clue 4, $M = 5$. By clue 1 and elimination, $O = 7$, $J = 9$. Then $H = 1$ (elimination).

**16. Perplexing Square #3.** $K = 9$, $L = 5$, $M = 6$, $N = 7$, $O = 4$, $P = 8$, $Q = 3$, $R = 2$, $S = 1$. By clue 1, the five odd numbers are K, L, N, Q, and S. So M, O, P, and R are the even numbers. By clue 2, either one row consists of three consecutive numbers in descending order reading left to right or one column consists of three consecutive numbers in descending order reading top to bottom. Since K, N, and Q are all odd numbers, the subject of clue 2 cannot be the leftmost column. Since both O and R are even it cannot be the middle column. Since both M and P are even it cannot be the rightmost column. If it were the top row, K and L would not both be odd. Since both O and P are even it cannot be the middle row. By elimination, the subject of clue 2 is the bottom row. Q is odd, and R is even and one less than Q (clue 1). Q is not 1, since R is smaller than Q (clue 2). Since $Q \times R = M$ (clue 4), the solutions for Q, R and M can only be $Q = 3$, $R = 2$, $M = 6$. So $S = 1$ (clue 2). $P = 8$ and $N = 7$ (clue 3). O is even, so it can only be 4. The numbers remaining to be assigned are 5 and 9. By clue 5, $L = 5$, $K = 9$.

**17. Perplexing Square #4.** A = 1, B = 5, C = 8, D = 2, E = 4, F = 6, G = 7, H = 3, J = 9. By clue 2, H = 3, and the product of H and J is a two-digit number whose leftmost digit is D. With H = 3, the product of H and J must have a leftmost digit of 1 or 2. D is not 1 (clue 1), so D = 2. By clue 1, the two-digit number with D as its leftmost digit and E as its rightmost digit is evenly divisible by C, D, E, F, and H. So that number must be 24. Thus, E = 4. Both C and F are factors of 24 (i.e., they "go into" 24 evenly), and neither is 1 (clue 3 and the fact that H = 3); so C and F are 6 and 8 in one order or the other; by clue 3, F is 6 and C is 8. The numbers that remain to be assigned are 1, 5, 7, and 9. Since 3 times J is a two-digit number with the leftmost digit being 2 (clue 2), either J = 7 or J = 9. J is not 7, as then H × J = 21, making G = 1, a contradiction of clue 4. So J = 9, and H × J = 27. By clue 2, G = 7. By clue 4, B = 5. A = 1 by elimination.

# ABOUT THE AUTHOR

Born near Richmond, Virginia, Margaret C. Edmiston received her A.B. from Upsala College, studied graduate psychology at Columbia University, and later received her M.A. in mathematics from West Georgia College. Following a long career in consumer marketing research, she now pursues writing, puzzle-making, and teaching mathematics. A longtime contributor to puzzle magazines under the names Margaret Edmiston, Margaret Shoop, and Sarah Brighton, among others, she has a continuing interest in writing for children and finds special joy and fulfillment in teaching mathematics as a member of the adjunct faculty of Virginia Commonwealth University.

Ms. Edmiston lives in Chesterfield County, near Richmond.

# INDEX

Page numbers in regular typeface=puzzle. Page numbers in italics=solving suggestions. Page numbers in bold face=answers.